R

The archaeological dig would only last for the summer, Mell knew, and then Barney would be gone again. But for now they would have fun together, with no strings attached . . .

RIDE A
WILD HORSE

BY

JANE DONNELLY

MILLS & BOON LIMITED
15–16 BROOK'S MEWS
LONDON W1A 1DR

*First published in Great Britain 1986
by Mills & Boon Limited*

© Jane Donnelly 1986

*Australian copyright 1986
Philippine copyright 1986
This edition 1986*

ISBN 0 263 75430 8

*Set in Monophoto Times 10 on 10 pt.
01–0886 – 62566*

*Printed and bound in Great Britain by
Collins, Glasgow*

CHAPTER ONE

THE boot fair on the old airfield brought in the crowds from miles around on fine Sundays, and today was a scorcher. Half the men, stallholders and strollers, were stripped to the waist and everybody was in the lightest of summer clothes.

The man sauntering past Amelia Beaumont's stall was tanned dark as mahogany. His skin gleamed, muscles rippled as he walked, and, beside Amelia, Pammie Moore gave a wolf whistle and collapsed in a fit of giggles.

The man turned and looked at Amelia with blank astonishment, then he saw Pammie and grinned and winked and walked on. 'Pack it in,' said Amelia, but Pammie went on giggling.

Pammie flirted as naturally as she breathed and usually it amused Amelia. Pammie meant no harm. She was always fancying somebody and because she was a pretty girl they often fancied her. If she could have lost a couple of stone she would have been stunning and she was usually on some diet or other and cheating all the way.

The boot fair meant, literally, sales from the boots of cars. Five pounds bought you a pitch and most Sundays saw a mixed bag up here, from folk hoping to unload household junk to professional traders. The professionals tried for the same spot each week, arrived with vans full of merchandise, and set up protective awnings.

Amelia had a small shop called Rainbow's End in the Cotswold town of Long Campden, where she made and sold clothes. Her slogan, 'Cheap, Cheerful and Colourful', was written across a rainbow on her van behind her pitch.

Pammie, her assistant in the shop and sometimes with the sewing, was eye-catching in Amelia's clothes. Blonde hair was in a frizzed halo and right now she was wearing a long loose caftan, with what looked like a firework display going on all over it.

Amelia was in a T-shirt and a wrap-over skirt, both in ice blue. She had an artist's eye for colour but bright shades did not suit her. She was pale skinned. She had kept out of the sun during this hot summer and she wore a floppy straw hat now, and the cool blue blouse was the colour of her eyes.

Pammie thrust a bag of fudge from the home-made sweets stall under Amelia's nose. 'Thanks.' Amelia took one and didn't mention the diet.

On glorious days like this the boot fair was fun. Families came and made a day of it, picnicking on the grass that grew beyond the tarmac. Hand-gliders floated overhead, launched from a nearby hill, and mingling with the voices and the music of transistors you could hear the whine of drag-racing cars, belting across the track at the far end of the airfield.

Pammie's current boyfriend was a drag-race enthusiast. She had arrived here this morning in his ancient souped-up Ford, and as she helped Amelia unload the van and watched Graham roar off she had said wistfully, 'It must be lovely to be driven around in a brand new Rover. Older men treat a girl with a bit of respect. I think your Robert's smashing.'

But as Amelia went on taking dresses out of the van and hanging them on rails she could have told Pammie that too much respect could make you feel very old. As usual she said nothing. She always kept her thoughts to herself. Her mother often said Amelia and Robert were made for each other. He was quite a lot older than Amelia, but she had always been a serious girl and she was lucky that a confirmed bachelor like Robert Gunnison had decided to share the rest of his life and his very comfortable home and income with her.

'I could do with an ice-cream,' said Pammie. Her face

was beaded with sweat. 'Hotter than ever, isn't it?' She collapsed on a packing case that threatened to give way beneath her weight. 'You wouldn't go and get me one, would you? I don't know how you manage to stay so cool.'

Amelia was warm, the sun was beating down on them all, but she wasn't suffering like overweight Pammie, who was surveying her puffy ankles ruefully.

'All right,' said Amelia, and set off between the rows of stalls towards the ice-cream van.

The van was doing a roaring trade, and she queued for a double-scoop strawberry ice-cream cone for Pammie—Pammie's favourite—and a frosted tin of Coke for herself. The ice-cream began to melt at once and she was hurrying back when she saw the man Pammie had wolf whistled at.

He had a pitch and a motley collection of goods, a big cardboard box of books, an old wind-up gramophone and records, and three trestle tables covered with bric-à-brac: china ornaments, plates, brassware, old jugs and bottles.

Junk, like fifty per cent of the stuff here. You could usually pick up something for a few pence. Amelia rarely bothered; her mother did not welcome bargains from the boot fair, although local antique dealers dropped in most Sundays with eyes peeled for a find. But of course most of the sellers knew the value of what they were offering and some of the prices were high. As Amelia glanced over this stall she noticed a china Cupid towards the back of the display. Fat and rosy, wings tipped with gilt, and a pink daisy-chain draped around it, one plump extended hand was broken, and she frowned, squinting at it.

'If it isn't Cheap, Cheerful and Colourful,' said the man, and she looked up at him, still frowning. She hadn't seen him here before; she didn't think he was local. In scruffy jeans, with the black hair and the deep tanned skin, he could be a gypsy, a tinker. She would have asked almost anyone else, 'Could I look at the Cupid?' but she didn't want him coming near her.

Instead, she went on staring at the Cupid because there was something there that intrigued her. Then she realised that ice-cream was dripping down her arm and splashing the front of her skirt and she swore softly and hurried away.

'Here, lick this quick,' she ordered Pammie, presenting her with the cornet and its rapidly liquefying contents, and Pammie's pink tongue curled around the pink ice-cream while she eyed Amelia's skirt and noted Amelia's frown.

'Sorry about that,' she said.

'Oh, it'll dry. I've just seen that man again. The one you whistled at. He's selling.'

'Why shouldn't he be?' Why should Amelia be frowning about that, Pammie meant.

'I wouldn't trust him an inch,' said Amelia.

'Who's asking you to?' asked Pammie. 'What *is* he selling? Something that fell off the back of a lorry?'

'That wouldn't surprise me,' said Amelia, surprising herself at the speed with which that came out when she knew absolutely nothing about the man, except that he irritated her.

'Do they wash?' a woman demanded, holding up a purple waistcoat.

'They're all colour-fast,' Amelia assured her, and took the money and put the waistcoat into a bag; Pammie, licking sticky fingers, said, 'Those seconds are going well.'

They brought a 'reduced' rail to the boot fair, garments with very slight flaws that Amelia did not consider quite up to her standard for her shop. Here they were a good seller and suddenly she realised what had caught her attention in the china Cupid.

It was the flaw of the missing fingers. A few months ago a house had been broken into about ten miles away. Two of her mother's friends lived there, and it was the usual sort of haul: video, hi-fi, TV, Mrs Palmer's mink coat and jewellery, silverware and some other small portable objects.

The little Cupid was Victorian, but the broken fingers would detract from its value. Everybody knew that stolen property often ended up in markets. 'Fallen off the back of a lorry' was common parlance, and she was going back to have another look because she was almost certain now that it was the little Cupid that had sat on one of Mrs Palmer's side-tables until the night of the break in.

She could very easily imagine him breaking and entering. He was what Pammie described as 'a bit of rough', which meant strong as an ox and capable of anything. 'I saw something on a stall just now,' she said to Pammie. 'I think I might buy it. Will you be all right for a minute?'

'Sure,' said Pammie. 'What?'

'A figurine. A Cupid.'

Once she had it in her hands she would know for sure; she had put her coffee cup beside Mrs Palmer's Cupid many a time. He would bluff of course, he was hardly likely to incriminate himself, so when she was sure perhaps she would buy it. When she went to buy the ice-cream she had passed a policeman she knew, off duty with his wife and two children, wandering round the market. She would get the Cupid and look for Bryan Jeffs and tell him what it was and where she had found it.

She was not going to enjoy this. 'Anything for a quiet life' was how she would have described herself, and when she got back to the stall and saw the Cupid had gone her first reaction was relief. 'Back again?' he said.

'Did you sell the Cupid?'

'Yes.'

'Who to?'

'A young couple. Their car was parked over there. They've gone.'

He looked straight at her and she could have said, 'Some friends of mine had one exactly like it, broken hand and all, taken from their home,' but she chickened out.

He might have turned ugly if she had suggested he was handling stolen goods. There were crowds around, it could only have been verbal abuse, but when he looked at her from under that thatch of black hair, she felt as she had done long ago when she had been half-way across a meadow and suddenly realised there was a bull in the field. Her mouth went dry and she went straight back to her own pitch.

'Didn't you get it?' asked Pammie.

'I missed it.'

So it had been sold and she could have been mistaken and now she would never know. Unless he had taken it off the stall after he'd seen her frowning at it, realising the Cupid was stirring memories and knowing it was 'hot'. His expression just now seemed to be challenging her to make an issue of it.

She served a customer with two dresses, feeling surer all the time that it *had* been Vera Palmer's Cupid. She wished she had let the ice-cream drip and made a closer inspection when she had first spotted it. She wished she had had the courage to meet his stare and say her piece when she went back and had at least let him know she knew. But that would have proved nothing; and he was a tough customer and Amelia had never gone looking for trouble.

She jumped out of her skin when he touched her shoulder. It was almost packing-up time by then. Most of the site was cleared and the crowds had thinned down to stragglers. The drag cars were still tearing down their track and Pammie would go over, to watch and wait for Graham, as soon as the 'shop' shut here.

'Why don't you come?' she'd asked Amelia, and Amelia was thinking about it, and lifting a cardboard box of assorted scarves into the van, when she felt a hand on her shoulder. She turned and there he was, and close up his powerful shoulders seemed to blot out the sun.

'Would you settle for this?' he said. He was carrying a large pot cat, with red spots on white, a long neck and an idiot grin. It was one of the ugliest things Amelia had ever seen. Vulgar and cheap, and Pammie said in a strangled voice, 'You weren't looking for something like that, were you?'

'Of course not,' said Amelia.

'I felt it had a certain charm,' said the man, 'and it's all I've got left in the china line.'

Pammie began giggling. 'I can see why it got left!'

He laughed. He had strong white teeth, and although Pammie was fluttering her eyelashes Amelia found nothing reassuring in this apparently friendly overture. He knew she knew. He was here to find out if she intended to do anything about her suspicions. Why else had he turned up with this ridiculous object?

Pammie was introducing herself. 'I'm Pammie, and this is Amelia, and who are you?'

'Barnaby,' he said.

'Why haven't I met you before? Where are you from?'

'I'm living in the old boathouse at Ruddington.'

'Well, you're the sexiest thing I've seen all week.' Put a personable man near Pammie and she immediately went into her routine. Usually Amelia took very little notice. Usually the men joked back, sometimes they backed off. It was just Pammie's way and, although Robert had no patience with her making such a fool of herself, Amelia was fond enough of Pammie to stand by with a wry smile.

But today she felt a fierce impatience as she went on loading the van while Pammie asked Barnaby Whoever-he-was if it was nice in the old boathouse and was he all on his own there?

'More or less,' he said.

Pammie should not be fooling with this one. Amelia knew that he was dangerous, and when he started to help dismantle the lightweight awning she said sharply, 'We can manage, thank you.'

'Speak for yourself,' Pammie gurgled, 'I can use all the gorgeous hunks I can get.'

Amelia bit her lip. She wanted to say, 'Shut up,' to Pammie, and, 'Go away,' to him, but instead she packed faster and let Pammie and Barnaby pull up the supports and tried to let their voices flow over her.

The set of her shoulders must have indicated her disapproval because while he was rolling up the awning Pammie put an arm round Amelia and coaxed, 'Come and watch the drag-racing. You don't have to hurry off, do you?'

Not tonight, thought Amelia. 'All right,' she said.

She finished the loading in silence. Pammie was telling Barnaby, 'We could do you a nice happy-jacket, any colour you fancy. I could measure you for it any time.'

He was laughing, but right now Amelia didn't think Pammie was all that funny. Amelia had problems enough; she could have done without this Cupid business. She was going to put that out of her mind because it was too late to do anything about it now.

She locked the back of the van. Pammie was still chattering, and the afternoon was still hot. Amelia leaned against the van so that her big-brimmed hat tipped over her eyes. She didn't have a headache but there was a *malaise* on her as though all was not well. I hope it rains soon she thought, I could do with something to clear the air.

He was watching her. Pammie was talking to him but he was looking at Amelia and this time she glared right back and he said, 'Cheerful and colourful? You've got to be joking!'

'That refers to my wares, not me. So does cheap.'

'That figures,' he said. He was trying to disarm her. He had a macho charm and knew it, a type that Amelia could not stand. She turned away and checked her bag for car keys and money and said to Pammie, 'Are we going to the drag-racing?'

'Ready,' said Pammie, and to Barnaby, 'and willing. Coming? I want to show you to Graham, and make him jealous.'

'Big is he?' said Barnaby.

'About half your size,' giggled Pammie, which was not true. Graham was a well-built, athletic young man, but this one could be a street fighter, Amelia thought. If it came to a scrap he wouldn't go by the rules.

Pammie slipped her hand through the bare muscular arm and Amelia stalked ahead with long fast strides. This time her tolerance had snapped. Pammie's teasing seemed infantile and embarrassing and Amelia steered away from them.

Running the stall was hard work. Afterwards she usually went home, to bath and change and get ready for the evening when Robert would be arriving. But she knew most of the drag-racing crowd and several called hallo to her as she walked towards the starting point.

There were no. two cars or motorbikes alike. The longest car was forty feet in length, the shortest a squat little model. Some had car wheels at the front, bicycle wheels at the back. Some looked comparatively normal, some had a touch of science fiction. But they had all been worked over, or built, with one aim—to reach the highest possible speed over the eighth of a mile track. Two hundred mph was sometimes reached, and some cars were fitted with drag-parachutes to slow them down once past the post and stop them ploughing into the hedges beyond.

They raced two at a time, matched for potential, and as Amelia walked up a couple shot away with a whoosh and a roar. There was a strong smell of bleach here. Dabbed on, it gave the wheels more spin and speed, and a sudden whiff of it made Amelia blink, and sneeze.

A slight breeze had risen and she pulled off her straw hat and let it stir her hair, which was thick and lustrous, and a deep honey colour. It fell from a centre parting, long and almost straight, and with her smooth forehead and wide grave eyes the effect was old-fashioned. When she wore a long dress she could have stepped out of one of those sepia photographs of girls who were called English roses before the First World War.

She was joined now by a lanky young man whom she had known for years. Alec Wilton worked in a garage and he saw that Amelia Beaumont's van and her mother's car got value-for-money servicing, but he had never asked Amelia for a date. She was a nice girl, but too serious. Nobody had been surprised when she had started going around with that solicitor who was old enough to be her father.

Now Alec told her how all the cars had performed and what speeds had been reached. Graham and Alec had both been pipped earlier. Amelia looked across to where Pammie, clutching the china cat, was introducing Graham to Barnaby, then looked away quickly and fixed her eyes on Alec, and pretended to listen. And watching was quite exciting. The explosive surge of speed that was over so quickly—whoosh they went, roaring down the track in clouds of dust; putting your foot down with the throttle wide open must be exhilarating and she wondered what Alec would say if she asked if she could have a go in his car some time.

Of course she wouldn't ask. There were women drivers here but they were all experienced. Amelia was a careful driver, but Robert would never let her drive his Rover. Women drivers worried him. When someone with longish hair infringed some rule of the road he usually sighed, 'Women drivers!' although quite often it turned out to be a man.

Perhaps it was as well that Robert had not let her drive the Rover if she had this subconscious urge to go like a bat out of hell. Up to now she had never gone more than slightly over the speed limit, but she was twenty-two at the end of the month and lately she had started to think about the things she had missed. Like being young. She had started to wonder if she had had any youth at all.

It was pleasant here, sitting on the grass, hands looped around her ankles, her long hair shadowing her face. The ground was hard and the grass was dry from the long hot summer, but it was nice to do nothing for a while, taking it easy. Alec gave her a running commentary as another two cars began to rev up, and Amelia tried not to see Barney Whatever-his-name-was.

She was conscious of him because of that wretched Cupid, and because of that she had the impression that he was keeping an eye on her, but suddenly she saw him coming towards her and scrambled to her feet. 'See you later maybe,' she said and left Alec gaping.

This was crazy, he was *stalking* her! He could do nothing to bother her here with all these folk around, but if she had walked any faster keeping away from him she would have been running.

And still he caught up. He was striding beside her, asking, 'What's the matter?' She stopped then and watched the cars so that she wouldn't have to face him and he said, 'You look like a girl with something on her mind.'

'I don't know what you're talking about.'

What was on her mind was the fact that he had had stolen goods on his stall. Well, one stolen item, but the evidence had gone and there wasn't a blind thing she could do about it. She had dodged the issue, she should have spoken up. How was she going to face the troubles that lay ahead when she was scared to raise her voice? Asking a stranger where something on his stall came from would be child's play compared with telling her mother and Robert that she was not at all sure she wanted an engagement ring for her birthday . . .

Over the roar of the engines and the scream of tyres there was an explosive bang and one of the cars with a blown tyre began veering wildly as the driver fought to control it. Everything happened so suddenly and so fast that she had hardly realised it was leaving the track and hurtling towards her before her arm was gripped and she was sent sprawling and the car went careering past.

Now everybody was shouting and running. The car stopped in the long grass and the driver fell out and staggered around, white as chalk. Miraculously, no one was hurt, although the car had ploughed straight through the spot where Amelia and Barnaby had been standing.

She was still lying flat where she had fallen, all the breath in her body squashed out by the impact of landing face down in the grass. But the car hadn't touched her and she tried to say, 'I'm all right.' He was all right, he was on his feet. 'Thank you,' she gasped, and of course she was grateful, although there had been no need to shove so hard.

The ones who had seen what had happened were saying it was a near thing and that it was a bit of luck, and Pammie came running over and Amelia got up and brushed herself down. 'I think I've had enough drag-racing for today,' she said. 'I think I'll be on my way. Er—goodbye.'

He said, 'Goodbye,' and Pammie and Graham went with her to her van. They offered to run her home and asked her if she was sure she was OK.

'Of course I am,' she said. 'It missed me, didn't it?' But she was gripping the wheel tighter than necessary and she had had a narrow escape. If that car had hit her it could have killed her, and although she might have got out of the way herself that very suspicious character had thrown her clear. But she wouldn't have been standing there if it hadn't been for him; she would have been sitting with Alec Wilton at the other end of the track. So, when you looked at it that way, she didn't have that much to thank him for . . .

The house where Amelia and her mother had lived for the past sixteen years was built in Cotswold stone, standing back from the road in a garden of flowers and lawns. The exterior was attractive but you had to step inside to appreciate that this was a very impressive residence.

Almost every item was a collector's piece. The paintings were originals, and family portraits, from delicate miniatures to a full-length oil of a whiskery gentleman, surveyed the intruder unsmilingly.

All this had come from a bigger house. Amelia had been five years old when her father had died in a car crash, and the family home had been sold because there was less money than anyone expected. Her mother had had a breakdown after her husband's death but she had still managed to select what should be held back from the auction out of all those rooms, so that the three-bedroomed house they moved into was converted into a Georgian gem.

Amelia parked her van round the side and heard her mother playing the piano as she opened the door. Elizabeth Beaumont was an accomplished musician, and when Amelia walked into the lounge she continued to play, although she looked up from the keyboard.

There had been a music room in the old house. In here, the piano dominated one end of the lounge, and Elizabeth, sitting at it, backed by the faded brocade curtains at the windows, made quite a picture.

She was a beautiful woman, her skin as pale as Amelia's, with dark, softly waving hair and spectacular violet eyes. Her wrists and ankles were very slender and everything about her seemed delicate.

Once she had had a household staff. Now there was only one ageing and arthritic woman who had never asked for wages because she was 'family', the occasional daily and Amelia. Elizabeth Beaumont tended her treasures, the Georgian furniture and silver, but she had never scrubbed a floor or peeled a potato.

'You're late,' she said to Amelia and waited for an explanation, the music still flowing softly beneath her fingers.

'I went to watch the drag-racing.'

'So noisy and dirty.' And dangerous today, thought Amelia, but she wouldn't get much sympathy; her mother didn't like unpleasant things. 'You'd better get washed and changed,' said Elizabeth, and her disapproving glance made Amelia conscious of the grass and ice-cream stains on her skirt and the dust that had settled on her face and hands. 'Robert will be here soon.'

On the dot of seven, thought Amelia, because Robert was a precise and punctual man. Tonight the three of them, Robert, her mother and herself, were going to a concert of chamber music, and her mother was ready. Elizabeth could have passed for Amelia's sister and the silver-grey silk suit she wore flattered her girlishly slim figure.

When Amelia said, 'I think I'm going to call off tonight,' a shadow of a frown flitted over her mother's brow and she stopped playing the piano. 'I've got a headache,' Amelia said, and by now she had, a small persistent nagging pain.

Amelia did not have headaches. Elizabeth had headaches; and rheumatic fever as a child had left her with a heart flutter that went into galloping palpitations when life became stressful. Amelia could remember very little of her father's death, but she could remember vividly nearly losing her mother. 'That poor child's going to be left on her own,' she had heard them whisper, and it had seemed to the five-year-old that the whole world was falling apart.

She had prayed for her mother all the time. Elizabeth's breakdown following John's accident had taken Elizabeth away until the big house had been sold and the small house had been ready to move into. She had gone to stay with friends in the South of France and Amelia had stayed with Nanny because Amelia had just started school and everybody had felt it would be better not to disrupt her routine.

Amelia had not missed the big house. Her last weeks there had been a nightmare, everything being moved, everything changing. It had been turned into flats, and when her mother drove past the gates she often sighed and looked wistful, but all Amelia could remember about that house was confusion and fear.

At first Elizabeth had wept for her lost acres and departed servants, and Nanny had comforted her. Nanny Demster had been Elizabeth's nanny when she was a child, and she had stayed on. When they first came to this house she was a big woman, strong-boned and a tower of strength. Now she had shrunk and her twinges played her up, but she had always been needed and loved and satisfied with her lot. Nanny thought Robert Gunnison was just the man for Amelia. She pooh-poohed the age difference. 'You always had an old head on your shoulders,' she told Amelia.

'But you never have a headache,' Elizabeth said shrilly.

'Sorry,' said Amelia. 'It's been hot and we were busy.' And Mrs Palmer's Cupid and the runaway drag-car hadn't helped.

'Then you should have come home when you packed up, not gone across to the drag-racing and all those fumes. And what are we going to tell Robert? He's paid for our tickets, you know.'

The town hall was hardly West End prices and Amelia said wearily, 'He could ask for a refund on mine,' and her mother shrilled, 'Don't be absurd!'

'Sorry,' Amelia apologised again. 'I'll ring him and tell him.'

'Tell him I shall quite understand if he doesn't want to go,' said her mother, looking and sounding martyred, 'Although Vivaldi is one of my favourites.'

'Of course he'll want to go.' Robert was always happy in her mother's company.

He was a partner in a law firm, a bachelor who had lived with a mother who ran his home with complete efficiency. When Mrs Gunnison died he was invited here and there, but he came more regularly to the Beaumont house than to any other and some people wondered if Elizabeth was setting her cap at him. She was not. She wanted him for Amelia. Amelia had realised that when he had had dinner with her and her mother a month after the funeral and had said it was kind of Amelia to be sitting through the meal with them when he was sure she could be out with her young friends having a much livelier time.

Her mother had said, 'Amelia isn't one of your

modern girls.' She had smiled sweetly. 'Modern young men don't appeal to her. Sometimes I wonder where it's all going to end. I shouldn't like to think of my daughter being a spinster.'

Amelia had gasped, although it was true, she didn't date much. She worked hard and she had never met a man who had stirred her to any great extent, but at twenty there was plenty of time.

'I'm sure there's no danger of that,' Robert Gunnison had said. 'I've handled so many divorces as a lawyer that I've always been wary of the married state myself, but I'm sure that Amelia's husband will be a very fortunate man.'

'Oh, he *would*!' Elizabeth had patted Robert's hand and Amelia had smiled unsteadily to hide her embarrassment.

But it was easy to like Robert, and it was easy to enjoy his admiration. She knew she was too serious for most of her contemporaries, but Robert liked quiet women. When she was with him she could concentrate on her day-to-day problems and let him do the talking, and he would look at her young thoughtful face and presume she was agreeing with what he was saying.

Most of the time she did. She had a pleasant time with Robert, who included Elizabeth in their outings more often than not, brought them both flowers and chocolates and small gifts, and whose favourite dishes Nanny prepared whenever he had a meal here.

It was a very suitable match. Right from 'early on when he took Amelia to the Hunt Ball, where the cream of the county was gathered, nobody said a word against it, because Amelia Beaumont looked the part of a well-to-do, middle-aged man's wife.

Pammie tried to tease her sometimes. 'What's your Robert like as a lover?' she'd asked and Amelia had said, 'He suits me.'

Pammie was not a sensitive soul; she never got the message until it was shouted out. Most folk would have accepted Amelia's quiet voice and cool steady gaze as the end of the matter, but Pammie went on, 'I expect he's ever so experienced.'

'Of course,' Amelia had said, turning away. She didn't tell Pammie to mind her own business, but she never discussed Robert with her, and for over a year now Robert *had* suited Amelia, nearly as well as his bank balance suited her mother and Nanny. They liked him very much, but if he had been a poor man neither of them would have considered him for Amelia.

Whenever Pammie met Robert she giggled and fluttered her eyelashes, and afterwards Robert usually told Amelia how glad he was that she herself was a girl with the right values. One of the right values was no lovemaking before marriage, except for some restrained kisses, frequent hand holding, and an arm around her shoulder. Amelia would go down the aisle in virginal white.

He had never actually asked, 'Will you marry me?' but she saw him several evenings a week, and when he entertained in his home or in restaurants Amelia was usually at his side. She had wondered at first if she was on trial but as time went by she presumed he had decided she was a suitable partner.

She supposed that she had been accepting it herself, but last week on the first of July Nanny had said she would have to see about Amelia's birthday cake. Birthday cakes were a tradition with Nanny, she created them as works of art. Amelia's birthday was on the twenty-eighth of July, and Elizabeth had smiled and asked, 'Can you keep a secret?'

The three women were alone in the house. They had been watching television and drinking milky nightcaps. 'I know what your birthday present from Robert is going to be,' she had said, 'but you must promise not to let him know I told you or it will spoil the surprise.'

Amelia had hoped he hadn't been too extravagant.

'His mother's jewellery,' Elizabeth had hissed, as if the room was bugged and this was treason. 'He told me yesterday but I wasn't to tell you, so it's all very hush-

hush.' She had put a finger to her lips, then taken it away again to say gleefully, 'There are some gorgeous pieces, and of course the ring. His mother's engagement ring. A beautiful big diamond cluster.'

'*Engagement* ring!' Nanny had said. 'Well, now! You mean they'll be getting engaged?'

'Of course,' Elizabeth had said, eyes dancing, lips smiling.

'Married, too, before long, I shouldn't wonder,' Nanny had added.

'Perhaps,' Elizabeth had said.

Amelia had said, 'He hasn't asked me,' but her mother had shrugged that off.

'He knows what you'll say. And the ring will fit, it's the same size as your pink pearl. But now you promise not to say a word or he'll never forgive me. You don't know a thing, either of you. Just act so surprised.'

Amelia had hardly slept that night. Robert should have asked her. He should not have been so sure. She was not sure at all . . .

The birthday present was not mentioned again. Her mother and Nanny kept their satisfaction in check, although there was an undercurrent of triumph in both of them. With Robert, Amelia simply could not get out the words, 'What's this about you giving me an engagement ring for my birthday?' She was incapable of precipitating a scene by asking him outright, because she did not want his ring. Not yet. Things were fine the way they were, but she was not ready to commit herself to his mother's engagement ring.

If she was even quieter than usual this week, nobody noticed. Robert had always chosen the wine and most of the food when they ate out. He guided her down the steps and into cars. He gave her hand little squeezes and her shoulder little pats, and told her what he thought about any subject that came up and was so sure she would agree with him that he never bothered to ask her opinion. He was not a whit more passionate; his kisses were always avuncular rather than lover-like. And the one thing Amelia had faced up to this week was that she was a coward. Because how she was going to tell them, she did not know.

When she told Robert about her headache he said that she must take a couple of aspirins and rest. He expected it was the heat and he felt that the boot fair was too much for her after working all week. He would miss her of course, but of course he would take Elizabeth along, he knew she had been looking forward to it.

Elizabeth came to Amelia's bedroom before they left to ask, 'You will be all right? Nanny's gone to Evensong. You'll be all right on your own?'

'Perfectly all right,' said Amelia. She was lying down but as soon as she heard Robert's car drive away her headache lifted and she sat up. She wasn't tired and suddenly her head wasn't aching any more so she came downstairs.

The house was very quiet. All her mother's cherished furniture was polished to a high gloss and not a thing was out of place. It was like a little museum, and Amelia went down the passage and opened the back door because she was feeling stifled.

She might as well drive round to the shop and unload. That would save time in the morning, and at least she knew what she was about there. She was fond of her shop, which was a riot of colour and was bringing in a steady income.

She left the van outside. Usually cars were bumper to bumper in the main road but on Sunday evenings there was parking space, and she carried in the boxes and rails of clothes. She was in the storeroom at the back when she heard the bell ring over the front door. It was late for customers but while she was here she was open for business and she came into the shop smiling.

The smile lasted only a second. It was that man again, and the walls of the shop seemed to close in until there was hardly room to breathe. He was a crook and he had tracked her here, but her panic was swamped by

anger at the nerve of him. She picked up a huge lump of
green glass, an old door-stopper that she had used
among a display of jade green skirts and shawls, and
held it in both hands.

'What were you thinking of doing with that?' he said.

'Throwing it through the window if I have to. And
don't tell me why you're here, I'll tell you.' There was
no backing down now. 'Yes' she said, 'I did recognise
the Cupid, and I do know where it came from.'

'So?'

For the first time in her life she had put herself in the
firing line. She clutched her door-stopper and raised her
voice. 'And I happen to know it was stolen property.'

CHAPTER TWO

'WHAT are you talking about?' He looked as if he was going to laugh and she said fiercely, 'It ws stolen from some friends of ours and I recognised it on your stall.'

'You don't say.'

Of course, she couldn't prove it, but she went on doggedly,

'From the Palmers of Teddington Road in Stratford. They had a break-in about six months ago.' This rush of aggression was making her light-headed but exhilarated in a queer way and quite capable of demanding of this hulking man, 'So where did you get it?'

'From the vicar,' he said.

'*What?* What vicar?'

'The Reverend James of St Elgar's. Mrs James gave me a boxful of odds and ends and I can't somehow see her or the vicar running a thieves' kitchen.'

That made her swallow before she could ask, 'Why should they give you anything?'

'Charity,' he said gravely.

'What charity?'

'The dig at Ruddington. Towards sustenance for the diggers.'

There had been something in the local papers about this. This summer's exceptional drought had revealed patterns of buried archaeological sites all over the country, and one was in a village called Ruddington a few miles away. Amelia had heard that an excavation had been planned and she supposed it was possible that he was at the boot fair raising cash to finance it. If he had had the Cupid from the vicarage it was unlikely to be hot. She asked, 'Was it Meissen?'

'Good lord, no.'

'Mind if I check?'

'Why should I?'

She had to put down the door-stopper, and she wasn't sorry because it was heavy, to get out the phone book and look up the number of the Reverend James of St Elgar's. Then she pressed the numbers and waited and felt like an idiot, because even if they had never heard of the man what was she going to do next?

'St Elgar's vicarage,' said a chirpy female voice.

'Mrs James?'

'My mother's not here at the moment. This is Susan James, can I help you?'

'There was a china Cupid at the boot fair today that I think came from your house.'

'Yes,' said the girl and Amelia knew for certain that she had boobed, although she went on,

'I missed it. You don't know where I could get another like it?'

The girl sounded puzzled. 'From a china shop or a gift shop I suppose. It wasn't anything special, you know. It wasn't antique or anything.' She laughed. 'Barney didn't tell you it was, did he?'

'Er, no, I just liked the looks of it. Thank you.' There must be thousands of china Cupids around, most of them modern copies. She put down the phone and said weakly, 'It looked like it. It had a broken finger and so did Mrs Palmer's.' Ornaments got chipped. There must be countless Cupids that had lost fingers but this one had been almost identical. Then suddenly she clapped her hand across her mouth and gasped, 'Rosebuds!'

'Citizen Kane,' he said promptly.

'What?'

'Forget it. You were saying?'

'Mrs Palmer's Cupid had a garland of tiny rosebuds, not daisies.' How could she have forgotten that? Because she had been prejudiced, that was why, and she shook her head at her own narrow-mindedness. 'I'm terribly sorry, but I was so sure. I suppose I thought you looked like somebody who might be flogging stolen goods.'

He grinned. He was still shirtless, he still looked tough as they come, but his grin was attractive and his eyes laughed, too, and thank heaven he could see the funny side of it. 'So that's why you picked up that hunk of glass when I walked in. What were you going to throw it at, the window or me?'

'I don't know.' No more did she, and much use that would have been as a weapon. 'It wasn't very gracious after you shoved me out of the way of that car. I must have been watching too much television, but you do look like a heavy. I mean, you'd never get cast as one of the good guys.' She grimaced, 'Sorry, I'm quite polite normally. I don't think I've ever slanged anyone before.'

He said, 'With practice you'd be an expert,' and instead of being embarrassed now she felt like laughing. She asked, 'What are you doing here?'

'I was on my way back to Ruddington and I saw your van as I passed by.'

'So you came in. Are you looking for Pammie?'

'I've just left Pammie and the rest of them in the Three Feathers. I was looking for you.'

'Why?'

If it had nothing to do with the Cupid why had he come up with the china cat? Why had he followed her at the drag-racing?

The shop had once been two rooms, but had been opened up long ago and the middle wall turned into an archway. He had been standing by the front door; she was still at the desk by the telephone at the back of the shop. He came nearer and stood, a tall dark figure, framed in the white archway. 'I'd never seen such a grave-faced girl,' he said. 'You never cracked the glimmer of a smile. I've been wondering ever since I first saw you what you'd look like if you smiled.'

'Why should I smile at you? I thought you were a crook.'

'Me and the vicar.'

She began to laugh until tears rolled down her

cheeks. She could use a little light relief these days, but she didn't realise how tense she had been until she sagged back into the chair behind the desk, wiping her cheeks with the back of her hand.

'You should smile all the time,' he said. 'It suits you.'

'Does it?' She liked his grin, too. It had more than a hint of the devil and it made her want to laugh. 'How did you do at the boot fair?' she asked.

'Not badly, considering all the stuff was donated. We're starting the dig in earnest tomorrow. The diggers are volunteers, most of them are students, sleeping in a barn, but funds are low and they'll need feeding.'

'I read about it. What are you doing? Apart from flogging Cupids at the boot fair.'

'Dogsbodying. It was a friend of mine who saw the markings of the villa first, when he was hang-gliding. Alan Whitehead. It's on land on his family's farm and we've got permission to do a summer dig.'

'Should be fun,' she said.

'Come and give us a hand.'

A new interest might not be a bad idea. It seemed that all she had ever done when the shop was shut was make herself useful at home and wait for Robert or somebody like Robert. She said, 'I've never done anything like that.'

'What kind of excuse is that?'

'Not much of one. I suppose there has to be a first time for everything.' She was conscious of the power and the confidence that he generated, and heard herself say wryly, 'I'll bet you don't have many more firsts to go.'

'A few,' he said. 'Come and see the site.'

'Now?'

'Yes.'

It was only a few miles away but it meant that Nanny would be back from Evensong before Amelia got home, and she would want to know how the girl who was too ill to go out tonight had recovered so fast and where she had been. Amelia hesitated a moment, but she was not a child, accountable for her every action. 'Let me finish unloading the van,' she said.

He helped her to carry in the remaining boxes and the awning, putting the boxes in the storeroom and the awning in the cellars which were her workroom. He asked questions, and in answering she told him that she lived with her mother and that that was all the family she had, except for Nanny who was like a grandmother. She had had the shop for three years now. Everything was made there. The clothes were simple styles; it was the patterns printed on them and the colours that made them original. Even after overheads she was earning a living.

'The crock of gold at the Rainbow's End?' he said and she laughed.

'There's no crock of gold; it's cheap, cheerful and colourful. I chose the name because I've always loved rainbows. What child doesn't? I used to think how lovely it would be to find a rainbow's end, but not for the crock of gold—just for the colours. To step from one to the other, all warm and brilliant.'

'Which colour would you have felt most at home in?'

'Red,' she said. He nodded as though that didn't surprise him, although it surprised her because she had never worn red in her life.

Light came down into the cellars through a barred grid, and from 'daylight' strip lighting. It was a large area of flagstoned floors and stone walls heated in the winter by oil heaters. A table for cutting out and an electric sewing machine stood at one end, with rails of clothes, mostly in cotton and linen, but a few in pure silk. At the other end was a desk with a slanting drawing-board, where Amelia worked out her designs, a table with a padded surface where she printed her fabrics, and another long shelf running the length of the wall and stacked with the tools of her craft.

Barnaby had been examining rollers and brushes and cutters and dye pots, and it seemed crazy that she had thought he was all brawn when she first saw him. After only a few minutes talk she knew that his mind was acute and perceptive and that he probably got more out of life than most folk. He had a surging vitality that seemed to stir the air around him and she thought drily, perhaps he'd make less impact if he had more clothes on.

He had an athlete's body, smooth and hard except for the dark hair curling on his chest, and maybe because she was an artist in her way she felt she could have modelled him in clay, kneading and stroking, and that she would like to touch him.

They emptied the van and he went ahead of her, out of the shop, while she made a final check around. Just inside the door was a big wicker basket full of scarves. She pulled out a wisp of silk the colour of holly berries, and tied it round her throat before she went out to join him.

His car was across the road. There were plenty of people out on this pleasant Sunday evening, tourists and locals. It wouldn't surprise Amelia if she was recognised. If she was, they would be wondering who her companion was, especially when they saw him open the car door for her to get in.

His car was one that you slid down into, and she settled herself and fastened the seatbelt. The car drew out and she watched the familiar street scene slip by, acutely conscious of the movements of the man beside her. Even in a heatwave Robert was always in collar and tie and lightweight suit. She could brush against Robert with no more sensation than touching a jacket on a coat hanger. But this was like sitting very close to a naked man.

The sun roof was open and the wind blew through her hair, sending it streaming back. His skin was dark against her own pale arms and sitting beside him made her feel like stepping into the warm red ray of the rainbow.

It was still light, but the first hints of dusk were misting the hedgerows. For a few minutes they drove in silence, then she asked, 'Is archaeology your job?'

'Yes.'

'What do you do, exactly?'

'Dig,' he said. 'Travel. I've taken the odd course, so I have some qualifications. I do freelance journalism, it gets me around.'

'A sort of hobo archaeologist?'

'That's it.'

She had not travelled much but when she had it had been to good hotels, because she was usually with her mother and Elizabeth never roughed it. Amelia had stayed with friends, who all lived in comfortable houses or villas, but Barney had probably roamed the world and gone to strange and savage places, sleeping on hard ground under the stars.

'Sounds fun,' she said wistfully, and realised this was the second time tonight she had said that. Fun was a childish word but it was something she had been denied, and, although maybe you could never catch up on wasted time, meeting Barnaby was opening up some intriguing possibilities.

A partridge came out of the grass verge, tripping with mincing steps into the middle of the road, and the car swerved to avoid it. It rose with flapping wings, flying low, then soaring overhead, and Amelia was jerked against Barnaby.

He swore. 'Stupid bloody bird!' and her face was flattened into his shoulder and he seemed hard as rock. It brought tears to her eyes. She straightened up as he straightened the car, and blinked and said, 'There's not much cushioning fat on you.'

'Sorry about that.' He grinned across at her. 'You prefer 'em flabby?'

'If I'm falling on them, yes,' she said, and he reached to touch her hand.

'All right?'

'Yes. I'm glad you missed it.'

'It's a straight road. There was no danger.'

But she could taste the sunburnt warmth of his flesh on her lips and where his fingers had brushed her wrist it was as though he had struck a pressure point of exposed nerves. The tingling sensation was running up her arm and down her spine, and she looked out of the window to smile because this was something she had never experienced before. She had been turned on.

She had wondered sometimes if she was frigid. Compared with Pammie she was, although she suspected that Pammie's affairs were mainly talk. Amelia had had her admirers before Robert, but they had all been undemanding. Possibly because with Nanny and her mother as constant chaperones they realised that it had to be all or nothing with Amelia. Marriage was the unspoken condition and they were never that keen.

She had never cared enough to take the initiative herself, so that she was very inexperienced for a girl of her age. She had been petted of course, and felt a slight stirring of the flesh when a man held her close, his mouth on hers, and wondered how it would be if the lovemaking went on. But when it didn't she was never desperately disappointed or frustrated. For the last twelve months it had been Robert, and his touch had hardly been electrifying.

Well now she knew that she was not frigid, and that if she let things take their natural course with this man she might experience something incredible. Her family was not going to intimidate Barnaby. In fact it was unlikely they would ever meet him, so the decision could be hers. He was attracted to her and here she was, nearly twenty-two, and nothing crazy had ever happened to her. The ends of the red silk scarf fluttered in the breeze and she went on smiling.

The river was low, it hadn't rained for weeks, but it was still fast flowing by the weir. She could hear the rushing water as they drove up the wide track towards the farm. The farmhouse was a big sprawling red-bricked building with twisting chimneys, and a weather-cock topped with the wrought iron figure of a running fox. Nobody seemed to be about and the car went bumping across a field between a flock of sheep, towards the river bank.

'Is this the field?' Amelia asked.

'The other side.' There were meadows there, too. He parked the car and they walked through a gate and over a bridge with the water foaming below, and now she could see a pattern in the grass, marked out in white.

'We did it from the aerial photographs,' he explained. 'It was a winged corridor villa, probably a farm; most of them were. The field boundaries showed, too.'

The plan was all there, the long veranda, the straight-walled shapes of rooms leading off. 'I wonder what they were,' she mused. 'The rooms.'

'We might find that out when we dig. This was probably the reception and dining area: the smaller ones would be offices, bedrooms, servants' quarters, baths—they were great ones for baths.'

'What would it look like?' She was standing on the site of what he thought was the living room and as he talked her imagination furnished a room around her until she could almost see the settle, stool, sideboard, a low table, murals on the walls, mosaic on the floor.

They went from 'room' to 'room', playing a game of him describing them as they might have been. The kitchen with its hearth and gridiron, tables and shelves, the shapes of pots and ewers, and she reached to where a shelf might have been and pretended to take down a vessel and set it on an invisible table. A bedroom, a couch; she stroked that and asked, 'Were the beds soft?'

'That depended on who was in them.'

'Not cushioned?' She opened her eyes wide and her lips twitched.

'What they lacked in cushioning they made up for in other ways.' He pulled her against him and she laughed because the hug was natural and joyous and he was laughing, too. It was nice to be held like this, fitting so snugly wherever she touched. She said, 'We are standing in the middle of an open field, aren't we?'

'No,' he said. 'We're in a Roman villa.'

'In that case I think we should get out of the bedroom and take a turn in the garden, if there is a garden.'

'You could be right about getting out of the bedroom,' he said, so they walked around the meadow, and he described and she 'saw' the courtyard and the orchard and the fields of waving corn.

'What happened in the end?' she asked.

'The fall of the Roman empire. Villas crumbled away, overgrown, taken apart. The Dark Ages took over.'

'The barbarians came down from the hills,' she said softly.

'In some cases.'

When she looked up into the darkening hills she thought they had probably hardly changed in two thousand years, and the man beside her, with his shaggy hair and tanned skin, might have looked at home among the marauders. 'You wouldn't make a bad ancient Briton yourself,' she joked. 'Barnaby the barbarian.' Then she remembered, 'Sue James called you Barney.'

'Most folk do. Do you shorten your name?'

'No.' If she had ever had a pet name it was too long ago to remember.

'Amelia's a mouthful.'

'It was a family name.' There was a miniature of Great-grandmama Amelia hanging on a wall at home. 'I always think it sounds mealy-mouthed, wishy-washy.'

'Well, that isn't you.' Not many would agree with him there. 'And if you don't like it what am I going to call you?'

'Will you be calling me anything?'

'Of course.' Even if she didn't turn up to help on the dig they would still keep in touch, she knew that. 'Would you answer to Melly or Mell?'

'I might.' She had felt different ever since she started to laugh in the shop just now, so perhaps she should have a new name. She tried 'Mell' for sound. 'Yes, I think I might answer to that. I suppose I should be getting home now, they'll be wondering what's happened to me.'

'Nothing's happened to you, yet,' he leered, and she said almost gaily,

'Promises, promises!' and thought of the times she had heard Pammie say that and didn't care, because clowning with Barney she didn't feel silly, just young and happy and full of life.

'Come in for a coffee,' he said. 'I'm staying in the boathouse.'

Pammie would have been up the ladder or whatever before the words were out of his mouth. Amelia wouldn't, but Amelia would not have been here, walking hand in hand with a man she had only just met, as easily as though she had been holding his hand, on and off, for years.

Even if she went home right away Nanny would probably be back so there was no point in panicking there. And Robert had booked a table at a good restaurant for a meal after the concert, so she could stay out another couple of hours and still get home before him and her mother. They would probably discuss her over dinner, settling her future, neither of them dreaming that she might have any plans of her own. 'I can't stay long,' Mell said. 'Not tonight.'

They went over the bridge again and he pointed out a big black barn where he said some of the student workforce were dossing down. There were no lights on and the doors were shut. 'Probably down at the pub,' he said. 'Most of them are arriving tomorrow.'

The boathouse was a little way down river, where a motor boat was moored under weeping willows. It was backed by a copse of trees, and a flight of wooden steps outside led up to the lofts.

She had expected a makeshift bed up here, maybe a folding table and chairs and the wherewithal to boil a kettle. She had thought he was camping out and she was surprised to step into a living room that was brightly, neatly, and fully furnished with a three piece suite with blue linen covers, red rugs on the dark-stained floor, dining section, and a bookcase containing some dog-eared paperbacks.

'It's a summer letting,' he explained. 'They've no bookings this month so they're letting me use it.'

He opened the door on to a tiny kitchen and offered, 'Coffee or a can of beer? The beer's cold.'

It was a hot night and her throat was dry. She said, 'Beer, please.' Her last drink had been that Coke at the boot fair. All she had eaten all day had been two pieces of fudge and a doughnut, and suddenly she was ravenously hungry. Usually she had a small appetite but now she was starving. She went to the kitchen door where he was taking two cans out of a small fridge and asked, 'Have you got anything to eat? I missed my dinner.'

'Cheese do? There's bread and pickles and fruit.' There was a punnet of strawberries and a bag of apples on the table. 'How did you come to miss your dinner?' He opened the two cans and handed her one.

'I didn't go. I should have been dining to soft lights and sweet music with a menu this long.' She held her hands ridiculously wide, although the bill of fare at Giuseppe's was pretentious.

'Let's see what we can do.' He opened a cupboard and she saw a few tins and packages. 'Baked beans, soup, or I could knock you up a special curry with a secret ingredient.'

'What secret ingredient?' She peered round him into the cupboard and howled, 'Not that tin of dog food?'

'The picture looks nourishing.'

'You knock one up for yourself,' she said. 'I'll have the beans.'

'How about spaghetti?' He came up with a long package. 'With butter and cheese and salt and black pepper?'

'Yes please,' she said.

He laid the table for two, with an assortment of china

and cutlery that didn't match, and put a candle in a red enamel candlestick in the middle and she asked, 'Are we expecting power cuts?'

'I suppose that's why it's here but I thought you might have been dining by candlelight.'

'Yes, I would have been.'

'With music you said.'

'Discreet background stuff. How are you going to manage that?'

He went into what was probably the bedroom and brought out a transistor, fiddled with buttons and came up with music, and set it on the sideboard to play softly.

'Do you know how to tell when spaghetti's cooked?' he asked her.

'Bite it, although you can usually tell when you look at it.'

'If you throw it at the wall and it sticks it's done.'

'Who told you that?'

'It's a well-known fact.'

'Do you do it a lot?'

'Not a lot. If you throw too hard it's not that easy getting it off the walls!'

The water was bubbling merrily and she tipped the beer can, drinking from it, letting the cool liquid trickle down her throat. He put a bowl of apples and the strawberries on the table and she examined the books on the bookshelf. They looked like holiday reading: romances, thrillers, westerns.

She thought she would like to stay here for a holiday with the river running just outside and all the basics for getting a meal, and beds and a bathroom somewhere. She would like to read the books, slumped in one of the easy chairs with her shoes off, and she would like Barney around. They could sit together and when it was night, really night, they could find a bed and lie down together.

A warm shiver went through her, and she took out a book at random and glanced through it. The doors

were thin. She could hear him splashing in the
bathroom and when he came out she supposed he
looked cleaner—it was hard to tell with his tanned
skin—and he was wearing an open-necked cotton shirt.

'Dressed for dinner,' she said. 'May I wash?'

She had swilled her hands when she came home and
splashed a little water on her face, but then she had
gone to her room and tried to rest and hoped the
headache would go.

In the little mirror on the bathroom cabinet she got
the full effect of her windblown hair. She looked like
Medusa and if she washed her face properly there
would be very little colour left in it. She relied on pink
blusher and lipstick and had neither here. So she
dabbed with a facecloth and called, 'Would you have a
brush or comb I could borrow?'

He handed her a comb and she tried to tug it
through, encountering some painful resistance. One
tangle made her yelp and he called, 'What's going on?'

'My hair feels as if it's been knitted.'

She literally had the comb stuck in a snarled-up hank
of hair and she put her head round the bathroom door.
'Any suggestions? Short of cutting it off. I could have
been in a hurricane the state it's got into.'

'Come here,' he said, 'and don't be so impatient.'

He sat on the sofa and she went and sat down beside
him, and the tangles seemed to slide away, he eased
them out so skilfully. She loved the feel of his fingers
against her scalp, running down the length of her hair,
stroking and teasing. She murmured, 'You'd have made
a super hairdresser,' and laughed as she said it.

'That depends on the kind of service you expect from
your hairdresser,' and with his hands still in her hair he
turned her face up to his and brushed her lips, lightly
but with a slow sensuousness that set her senses singing.

She knew it meant no more to him than their hands
linked in the meadow but it was the most enjoyable kiss
she had ever had. Robert kissed so seriously. He never
looked at her afterwards, smiling as though that had

been good, and there was never a question in Robert's eyes—do we go on? That kiss could be starters. She could be ravished here and now if she was willing.

'Do you think the spaghetti's ready?' she said.

'Not quite.' But he went on combing and brushing her hair and the moment passed.

It was all easy and unforced. She had never eaten a meal with anyone with whom she felt so relaxed. The steaming spaghetti, piled high on the plates, smooth with butter and spiced with cheese and black pepper, was delicious. She twirled it around her fork and the butter ran down her chin, and they talked and talked and she seemed to spend half the time choking with laughter.

He made her laugh. 'You're a clown,' she told him, while he was describing some of the characters who would be working on the dig, and she couldn't believe that when she saw him first—only this morning, and that was incredible, too—she had been scared of him.

He remembered half a bottle of white wine still in the fridge and brought it out and they poured it over the strawberries and dipped them in sugar.

'Where did you get the strawberries?' she enquired. It was strawberry picking time. Pick-your-own boards were outside the fruit farms. 'Did you pick them?'

'No, they arrived some time today.'

A present! And she bet he knew who had picked them for him.

'Who should you have been having dinner with?' he asked. He dipped a huge scarlet strawberry and offered it to her, and she looked at his hands and thought of Robert's plump pale fingers and felt that she would not have cared much if Robert never touched her again. But when she took the strawberry she had a terrific urge to lock her sticky stained fingers with Barney's even if it did mean squashing the strawberry.

'My mother,' she said, 'and a friend.'

'Whose friend? Yours or your mother's?'

'Both,' she said, and then, 'mine, I suppose.'

'Special?'

Her mother and Nanny and Robert certainly wanted him to be special. 'Not exactly,' she said.

'That'll do.' Barney smiled and she bit into the strawberry he had given her. 'Why didn't you go tonight?'

'I had a headache.' He raised an enquiring eyebrow. 'It's gone. Do you have anyone special around?'

'No,' he answered promptly; but someone had picked him strawberries, although it might be just some kind and motherly soul. Of course there were girls; he would attract them anywhere. He had so much magnetism they must come in droves, and if he made a habit of propositioning as fast as he had with Mell most of them would imagine they were special.

Goodness she thought, how cynical I am, and she was pleased with herself for being so astute. She said, 'It's been a lovely meal, I've enjoyed it immensely.' She licked her sugary fingers. 'What with my hair and the butter and this I can't remember ever getting into such a mess.'

'A very appetising mess,' he said. 'And now you have to go home?'

'Yes.'

'You could stay.'

Nobody ever asked me to stay the night before. He'd be shaken if he knew how inexperienced I am, she thought, and that amused her. 'Thank you,' she said sweetly, 'but not tonight,' and realised that amounted to an unspoken promise.

She washed her hands and he drove her back to the shop and her van. On the way they discussed how she might manage a few hours from the shop to get over to the dig. They usually knocked off around six, he told her, working later if necessary. She closed Thursday afternoons, she could come then, and if she could arrange things with Pammie she might take some extra time off.

'It's labourers you want, isn't it?' she joked. 'You're working on getting a free workforce.'

'Of course. As soon as I saw you I thought, now there's a big strong wench who could handle a spade.'

'I might come dearer than you think.'

'I thought the cheap and cheerful was too good to be true.'

He looked up at the slogan painted around the rainbow motif on her van and in the corner of the window, and grinned. She laughed, too, and said, 'I am too good to be true,' and thought, such nonsense we're talking and it's fun and I feel sixteen.

'I'll see you tomorrow,' he said.

'Soon anyway.'

'Very soon,' he said, 'now I know where to find you.'

Nanny was on the lookout for her. She had probably been watching through a window for the van because she came out of the house as Mell drove round. The van stood outside, there was only room for one in the garage.

'Your mother left a note to say you weren't feeling well and you were having a lie-down,' said Nanny. 'Then I find you gone.'

'I'm all right.' Mell walked into the house and into the kitchen because that light was on. It was a big kitchen for the size of the house, but the aroma from the pot of darkish mush simmering on the stove filled it. Nanny was making strawberry jam. Her store cupboard was one of her prides, but Mell knew that this activity, latish on Sunday night, was because she was worried and couldn't settle down.

'I had a headache,' Mell said, 'but I took some pills.' That was a lie, she hadn't taken pills, but she couldn't tell Nanny that the headache cured itself as soon as Robert's car drove away. 'And when I felt better I took the stuff from the market back to the shop.'

'But you didn't stay at the shop, did you?'

So somebody had seen her leave with Barney and been nosy enough to ring here about it. One of Nanny's gossipy cronies, or one of her mother's snobbish friends. Amelia Beaumont, as good as engaged to

Robert Gunnison, getting into a car and driving off
with a rough-looking customer, would soon be going
the rounds.

'Who is he?' wailed Nanny. 'I didn't know what to
say. Hilda Hallchurch ringing me and asking who your
new boyfriend was.'

'Hilda Hallchurch is jumping the gun,' said Mell.

'She said he looked like a gypsy.'

'A hobo,' said Mell, and couldn't help smiling. 'But
very well-spoken. Actually he's an archaeologist and
he's here to work on the dig at Ruddington.'

'What's a dig?' said Nanny. That news item in the
local paper had escaped her, and anyway she didn't
want to know. She was completely preoccupied with the
fact that Amelia had called off her date with Robert
and gone out to meet another man. Somebody so
unsuitable that Hilda had been breathless with
excitement.

'How long has this been going on?' she demanded as
Mell started to tell her about the villa.

'What?'

'How long have you *known* him?'

'I met him at the boot fair this morning. He saw my
van outside the shop and looked in and we started
talking about the villa and he took me over to show me
where they're going to dig for it!' Nanny looked,
wordlessly and accusingly, up at the clock on the wall.
'We had spaghetti and a can of beer and a punnet of
strawberries,' said Mell.

'And that's all it was? You hadn't arranged to meet
him? It was an accident?'

'A sort of head-on collision,' said Mell. Everything
about her was frightening Nanny. The old woman
wanted to hug her and hold her, because it was as
though the girl was straining to get away.

She said, 'You won't be seeing him again?' but
without much hope.

'I'm going to help on the dig in my spare time,' said
Mell.

'What's Robert going to have to say to that?'

'It'll be none of Robert's business.' But as Nanny sat down heavily in the nearest chair, Mell said gently, 'I've been thinking for quite a while about this. It's nothing to do with Barney, I really did meet him for the first time this morning. But whether I want to get engaged, whether I'm ready. I haven't even been asked yet. Robert's taking it for granted that I'm here and waiting and I don't know if I want to spend the rest of my life with him.'

Nanny shook her head, slowly and sorrowfully. 'Your mother's got no idea you're feeling like this. It's going to upset her.'

Elizabeth was always Nanny's first concern, her violet-eyed baby who had suffered so much. She said plaintively, 'If you marry Robert you'll want for nothing,' and Mell thought, how do you know what I want?

She said, 'Money isn't everything,' and Nanny retorted, 'You're a silly girl,' and Mell thought, I wouldn't mind being silly for a while.

'It'll end in tears,' said Nanny, trotting out a warning from long ago and Mell smiled at her and said, 'I'm only asking for a little time before I settle down. I don't want to get engaged on my birthday, that's all. Can I help with the jam?'

'I can manage, thank you,' said Nanny huffily, getting up and going to the stove, keeping her back turned until Mell left the room.

She was annoyed and she was upset and both reactions Mell had expected. She had been dreading breaking the news that she did not want that ring, but now it was out and she could face the fuss because it was her life they were arranging and it was high time she had a say in it.

She took a quick bath and heard Nanny come up to her room, the stairs creaking under her slow arthritic tread. The car hadn't come back yet so her mother would not be bursting in here tonight demanding to know what it all meant and if Amelia was going out of her mind.

She sat up in her bed brushing her hair, the way she always did last thing, saying her name to herself over and over. 'I am Mell, Mell.' And it seemed that even her hair, which usually fell smooth and heavy from the brush strokes, was springing back tonight as if it was generating more electricity.

Her life could have ended today and up to now it hadn't been much of a life. For the rest of the summer she was going to have some fun, act her own age, not Robert's. Tomorrow she would choose a dress and it would have red in it; the red scarf hung over a chair back and it was a marvellous colour.

She would go over to the dig, make new friends and get her hands dirty, and before long Barney would make love to her. The thought of that melted her so that her hands dropped limp and helpless and she lay back on the pillow, weak with desire.

She was so lucky to have met Barney just when she needed someone exactly like him. At the end of the summer dig he would be on his way and in the meantime he could show her how to live a little. She was surely entitled to a few carefree months, and Barney with his zest for life would be a fantastic teacher.

Barney ... Barney ... She didn't even know his surname. Although they had talked and talked he hadn't told her very much about himself. But there was a wildly exciting rapport between them, and that was enough to send her happily to sleep, blotting out the memory of her first impression that he was a most dangerous man.

CHAPTER THREE

SHE felt different from the moment she woke. Nothing else had changed. The room was the same with its pretty Victorian furniture, the early morning sun was streaming in through the white muslin curtains—no rain again from the looks of it. But she woke as Mell, with the new restlessness getting her out of bed and under the shower as if she had a plane to catch and not a moment to lose.

Heaven knows she knew how she looked, but this morning she walked from the bathroom with a bath towel around her and dried herself in front of the cheval mirror in her bedroom. Her body was all right, her stomach flat, her breasts firm. She was hardly voluptuous, but she had long slender legs and she was quite presentable naked. Not that she was aiming on stripping off, but it was pleasant to know, and she finished drying herself and dressing and slapping on her usual moisturiser and blushers.

Everyone knew the saying, 'This is the first day of the rest of my life,' but this morning she could almost have said, 'This is the first day I have really been alive.' There was this marvellous excitement in her as if all sorts of promises and possibilities lay ahead. She couldn't wait to start living this day.

Downstairs Nanny was up. Once she was always the first out of bed but for the last two years it was Mell, often as not, who prepared breakfast and lit fires when the mornings were cool. Nanny usually had a cooked breakfast of bacon and eggs, Mell had coffee and some sort of cereal, unless she was in a hurry when she skipped the first meal altogether, and Elizabeth took tea in bed and came down later to more tea and wafer-thin toast. Elizabeth was never first up.

This morning the table was laid and Nanny was sitting down with a cup of tea. A row of jars filled with jam stood on the Welsh dresser, proof of last night's industry, and there was no smile for Mell this morning. 'That colour doesn't suit you,' Nanny declared. 'Makes you look pasty.'

The red scarf probably looked like a flag of defiance. 'I am pasty,' said Mell cheerfully.

'Are you going to tell her?'

They were carrying on last night's conversation as though there had been no break, and if Nanny had not been worrying about it during the night she had certainly been sitting here brooding this morning. The kettle was full and hot; Mell spooned instant coffee into a cup then pushed the kettle's On switch and it boiled within seconds. She said, 'It isn't that earth shattering. I've just decided I don't want to get married yet.'

'You mean you're turning Robert down.'

'Not really,' Mell pointed out. 'I'm not even supposed to know he's got a ring for me.'

The coffee was scalding hot but she tried to sip it, and Nanny got slowly to her feet and went through the routine of making a cup of Earl Grey tea with a slice of lemon and no sugar. She said nothing until the four minutes brewing time were up, when she poured the tea from the little pot and said, 'Here, take this up.'

Elizabeth always had the same cup; well, one of the seven left out of the original twelve; beautiful white china, eggshell thin and gold patterned. It was a major calamity when any of the old china was broken. Mell had dropped one of these cups on the flagstoned kitchen floor years ago and hidden for hours in the attic, too scared to come out. Upsetting her mother had always been the greatest sin and this morning Elizabeth was likely to be very upset indeed.

Mell put the cup on the bedside table and drew back the curtains; light flooded the room. The woman in the bed sat up yawning, 'Morning, darling. Headache better?' She didn't wait for an answer. 'The recital wasn't that good, you didn't miss that much. I've heard the *Four Seasons* played much better.' She reached for her tea, 'Could you do some shopping for me today? There's a list on the dressing-table.'

Mell had thought she might dash over to the dig at lunchtime, just to see what was happening. 'I've got a coffee morning,' said her mother languidly as though that was going to take all her strength, although she wasn't giving it, just going as a guest to a friend's house. 'And then I have to get my hair fixed.' She blinked suddenly over the teacup, her eyes and her voice sharpening. 'What have you done to your hair?'

'Nothing,' said Mell and looked at herself in the dressing-table mirrors. 'Brushed it back I suppose.' At any rate it wasn't falling over her face this morning. She said, 'Nanny thinks I should talk to you. I was telling her last night that I don't want that engagement ring from Robert.'

'What?' Elizabeth's voice was very faint.

'I've been worrying about it ever since you told me. It wouldn't be fair on Robert. It wouldn't be fair on me either because I don't feel ready to settle down.'

Very deliberately Elizabeth replaced her china cup and saucer on the little table, then she clasped her hands together and sat, head on one side, intent and watchful, and Mell went on, 'I'd always be wondering what I'd missed.' A soft gasp came from her mother, almost a whimper. 'I've led a very sheltered life. I've been happy of course, but I want to be sure it's what I want for the next fifty or sixty years.'

'You've met someone else.' Elizabeth made it a shuddering accusation, as though Mell had been caught out in behaviour that was almost obscene; but although there was Barney, he was not the cause, so she was wrong there.

Mell said, honestly, 'It's my birthday coming up. I'm not quite twenty-two, but I feel so old.' This morning she felt her right age but it was the first time for years. 'There was the ring waiting and everyone taking it for granted that I'd do what was expected of me because I always have.'

'But—you and Robert—he's so right for you, he loves you——' her mother wailed.

Robert liked her, maybe he loved her, but she wanted to experience something wilder and more exciting. She wasn't ready for a permanent nest, she wanted to spread her wings.

Nanny appeared in the doorway and Mell said, 'I told her,' and Nanny glared, although she had been insisting that Mell did just that, and swept across to the bed like a nurse with a patient, taking Elizabeth's hand as if she was taking her pulse. 'There, there,' Mell expected her to say. She said nothing, but both women sighed and both fixed reproachful eyes on Mell.

They were trying to put a load of guilt on her and she resisted the impulse to promise them anything. Instead she said, as lightly as she could, 'It isn't that big a deal. You don't need to look as though I'm turning to crime because I don't want to get married yet.'

Her mother's face was pale and Nanny said brusquely, 'Get along with you, you don't know what you're doing.'

Mell took the shopping list and left them. This was the first time ever that she had not fallen in with their plans and she was in for a stormy session. But she was right. Unless she believed they would be happy together there was no reason why she should marry Robert. Her mother would have liked a wealthy son-in-law, but Mell knew that they were financially solvent. They wouldn't go bankrupt if Mell didn't grab a rich husband.

Robert might be offended but now her mother could forewarn him and he wouldn't produce the engagement ring so his pride need not be hurt. You couldn't reject a man who hadn't offered.

She passed the glass-fronted case of miniatures on the wall at the bottom of the stairs, with the tiny portrait of Great-grandmama Amelia looking out, smooth-haired, smooth-faced, her mouth pink and prim, her eyes beady bright; and she looked disapproving, too. 'I'll bet no one ever called you Mell,' Mell muttered, and just like last night she couldn't get out of the house fast enough.

Outside, the day was dazzling. Inside, lace curtains usually kept out the glare of the sun because it faded old carpets and tapestries and showed up the worn spots. When she stepped outside she had to shade her eyes for a moment.

This was going to be another scorching day. Digging the dig-field would be hard work. Even tending a cultivated garden had been tough this summer, with its record low rainfuall. She noticed that, snaking across the parched lawn, through an arch in a copper beech hedge, was a blue garden hose.

Mell turned off the tap at the back of the house to which the pipe was attached then followed it. Beyond the arch was the rose garden, and among the roses was a small wiry man spraying the garden hose over the bushes. As she reached the arch, the flow of water became a trickle.

'Watty!' she called and he jumped.

'Morning,' he said sheepishly.

'You'll get caught you know.' There had been a ban on hosepipes and sprinklers for months, but Walter Cheever had regular memory lapses and now he chuckled.

'What the eye don't see . . .'

'*I* saw. Anyone coming to the back door would see it. A bright blue hose, it stands out like a sore thumb.'

'Maybe I'll get myself a green 'un. Or yella if it goes on like this. Hot again, isn't it?' he said. 'Any chance of a cuppa?'

Like Nanny, Watty had always been part of Mell's life. He had been a gardener at the old house, staying on when that house was turned into flats but always keeping this much smaller garden in trim. He had retired from full-time employment about five years ago, and now did jobbing gardening and was here most days.

You could rely on Watty. He never seemed to change. He had always seemed as gnarled and brown and thin as an old nut tree. Then there was his cap. Summer and winter Watty wore a flat check cap. You looked for the cap and Watty was under it.

He cared for this garden for a pittance and he loved it. Over the years he had come to think of it as his own. Out of sight of the house in the potting shed he smoked his pipe and knocked back his cider, and entertained old mates who came in stealthily by the back gate.

Mell suspected that Nanny was another reason he came so regularly. They had been warring as long as Mell could remember, and both of them enjoyed having an old and reliable antagonist. When Watty was bored he could always traipse dirty boots over the kitchen floor, and when Nanny's twinges played her up she could always go and root Watty out of the potting shed.

'No. And I'd keep out of Nanny's way today.'

'Summat in the papers was it?' asked Watty. Nanny's temper was often sparked off by the headlines, the news these days did that to lots of people; or it could be the arthritis. He was mildly curious why it would be wise to keep out of her way for a while, but when Mell said,

'It was me, I've upset her,' he said incredulously,

'You never upset anyone in your life, m'dear, it isn't in you.'

Mell's smile was rueful. He had meant it as a compliment. Right from a child she had never troubled or disturbed anything, not even a flower bed, but she had stirred up a small storm today. 'Put it this way,' she said. 'You're more likely to get the kettle chucked at you than a cup of tea this morning.'

'That bad?' Nanny Demster was an old battleaxe but she had never actually thrown anything at him. Amelia had to be joking, but he would keep out of the kitchen.

*   *   *

Pammie arrived for work at nine, unless she had an excuse for being late, which was not uncommon. This morning at five to nine there was no sign of her and Mell picked up the mail from behind the door, gave it a quick glance—four envelopes, none looking urgent—put it on the desk and went towards the clothes rails.

She knew what she wanted. She had been thinking, and she took down a white skirt with a pattern of huge poppies running around it, and then a white shirt with a single poppy. She got out of her pale blue dress, into shirt and skirt, and she was in the changing cubicle when she heard the doorbell ring and Pammie called, 'Yoohoo. Anybody home?'

'I'm in here,' Mell called back, fastening the waist button.

'We went to the Three Feathers last night.' Pammie had come down the shop and was probably at the desk looking at the post. 'They've got a very good salad bar, if you like salads.' Most of her diets included salads and she did not like them. 'I had the carvery,' she said. 'With roasties. I love roast potatoes. And Yorkshire pudding. You know I lost three pounds last week.'

'Yes,' said Mell who was told every time Pammie weighed herself.

'Well I'm not going to weigh myself again till Thursday,' said Pammie. 'Barney came with us. He wouldn't stop for a meal but isn't he dishy?' Mell guessed she was rolling her eyes. 'He's going to be here till September. Over at Ruddington, where they found those ruins. Do you know what he does?'

'Yes,' said Mell.

'Do you? How do you know?'

The skirt fitted Mell's narrow waist snugly; it would swirl when she twirled. She liked what she saw in the mirror. She put hands on hips and smiled, telling Pammie, 'I was unloading the van when he drove past here and he came in. He told me about the dig and I went over to see. All there is right now is the plan marked out, but it was interesting.'

There were a few moments while Pammie digested that, then she said, 'I'll bet it was.'

Mell pulled the curtain and came out of the cubicle and Pammie whistled soundlessly and blinked and, after another pause, gasped, 'You've brightened your ideas up.'

'Don't you think it was about time?'

'Yes. Why not? But what——?' And then, as though understanding was dawning, 'I *see*. Last night? *Him?*'

Everybody thought it was Barney, as though just meeting him had transformed her, and that wasn't true. 'No,' she said. 'It's my birthday on the 28th. I'll be twenty-two, and I suddenly realised I've led a very boring life.'

'I thought your life was the way you liked it,' said Pammie. 'You never complained.'

'Could be I'm a late developer. Most kids break out in their teens, I've waited for my twenties.'

Pammie still looked bewildered. 'You just suddenly feel like breaking out?'

'Yes I do.'

'Just because it's nearly your birthday?'

'Because everyone thinks I'm due to settle down with Robert.'

Robert Gunnison's money and house and car would have been very tempting to Pammie. Amelia would never have to work again if she settled for Robert, and Pammie thought that couldn't be bad. But she hadn't said a word about being fed up before, not even yesterday, and Pammie began to grin, knowingly. 'Yesterday Barney turned up. Did you, last night—you know?'

'No,' said Mell.

'I believe you.' Pammie's grin widened to a leer. 'But I can see that a bit of my laddo would put old Robert in the shade; Robert is a bit of an old woman. Just went over and looked at the field, did you?'

'We had supper,' said Mell. 'In a flat over a boathouse.'

'The two of you? All on your own?'

'Mmm.'

'What did you have?'

'Spaghetti.'

'Well it's fantastic what spaghetti can do. I'll have to try it; you look a different girl this morning.' Pammie went into splutters of merriment and Mell found herself smiling, too.

'I'm going over to the dig. It's fascinating, wondering what was there all those years ago, what they're going to turn up. It'll be a new hobby.'

'You've never had a hobby before have you?' said Pammie emphasing the word, giving it a double meaning.

Pammie was right. Mell's work and her shop had filled most of her life. She looked at the mail now, all business letters, then went to turn the Closed sign to Open on the door. Pammie answered the phone on the desk when it rang.

'Rainbow's End, can I help you?' Then a giggle. 'Won't I do? You don't know what you're missing.' She held the phone towards Mell. 'Your new hobby's on the line.'

'Barney?' Pammie nodded. 'Hallo.'

'See you mid-day?' he said.

She hadn't promised to go over. She had said she would try, maybe lunchtime, maybe after work. 'I don't know that I can manage that,' she said now. 'I've got some shopping to do.'

'Do you know the Angler's Arms?' It was a pub half-way between Ruddington and here.

'Yes.'

'I'll meet you in the bar as soon as you can make it. What do you eat? I'll get it in.'

'Oh sandwiches, anything.' She laughed. 'Except curry!'

'Not even with the special ingredient? Right. See you.'

She was still smiling when she put down the phone and Pammie said, 'Don't you like curry?'

'It's a joke,' said Mell.

'Oh.' Pammie hesitated then said, 'Can I give you a bit of advice? I mean, you haven't knocked about a lot have you and I think you ought to be careful about Barnaby. He's a hard nut, you only have to look at him to know that, and he *has* been in prison.'

'Has he?' That was a shaker.

'Didn't he tell you? I suppose he didn't think it counted as it was abroad, but inside's inside, isn't it?'

'What was it all about?' asked Mell.

'Oh, somebody in the Three Feathers had just come back from holiday, staying in some village in the Greek islands, and he said the last time he was there he landed in the local nick.'

'Well he got out again,' said Mell. And it couldn't have been anything too terrible or he wouldn't have been chatting about it to comparative strangers.

'Will you take him home to meet your mother?' asked Pammie, with slight malice because Elizabeth Beaumont had never made Pammie feel very welcome.

'Why should I?' After Robert, her mother would disapprove of Barney on sight.

'I wouldn't if I were you,' said Pammie. 'And I can't see old Nanny going a bundle on him either.'

Mell shrugged, but silently she agreed. She could imagine the expression on both their faces if Barney turned up at her home because, although Mell loved them both dearly, there was no denying that they were appalling snobs.

Downstairs, in her workroom, she put on an enveloping, paint-stained smock and began mixing the dye-paste for her morning's printing. It was a kingfisher blue and she stirred it to the right shade and consistency. All the procedures of her craft were second nature to her; she did them automatically, but they still gave her a quiet satisfaction.

The material was draped over the padded table, everything was set out in its proper place, to right and to left, and she poured the dye into a palette tray and transferred it by roller on to the wooden block on which she had carved the design of a flying bird. She pressed the block home firmly, leaving a clear sharp pattern on the pale blue material. Later she would add little white clouds, but first she printed blue birds. Although she had decided on Friday to do this pattern today, blue birds suited her mood this morning.

Pammie was in the shop, coming down occasionally to report a sale, and sometimes because she couldn't get over the change in Mell.

She brought down a mug of coffee at eleven o'clock—there was an electric kettle in the storeroom off the shop. Mell always had black coffee with one spoonful of sugar and Pammie asked as she came downstairs, 'You don't want cream with it?'

'No thanks. Why?'

'Well, like I say, you're a different girl this morning. I thought your taste in coffee might have changed, too.' She was joking but she wasn't entirely happy. Amelia, the way she was, had suited her fine. Mouselike, no competition, a nice girl but no sparkle to her. It was hard to believe that that super sexy feller had met up with Amelia last night and taken her over to his pad and rung her again this morning arranging to meet her. Pammie would have thought that if he had swept her off her feet last night she would have been shaking in her shoes this morning.

Instead she was laughing. When she took the coffee and said, 'My tastes in some things have changed, but not in coffee,' there was a hint of recklessness that Pammie had never seen before. That tale about suddenly deciding for no reason she wasn't settling for Robert was rubbish, of course, so something pretty incredible must have happened between those two last night. Up till now Pammie's envy of Amelia's middle-aged lover had been half-hearted but this was a very different thing.

They shut the shop from half past twelve to half past one. Pammie was eating her lunch in the office, but she watched through the window as Mell hurried along the road, the sun glinting on her flying hair, the bright poppies on her skirt making an eye-catching blur of colour. Men's heads turned as she passed. Pammie had never seen that happen before and as she went into the office, to face her crispbread and low-fat cheese-spread lunch, she muttered, 'You're going to make such a fool of yourself.'

Mell whizzed through her mother's shopping list. Tights, 10 denier, and pearl grey—she knew the make and the shop. A pack of non-prescription painkiller pills that Elizabeth carried with her. She had stronger pills for migraines; these were for slight headaches, little pains. And some make-up. Elizabeth was loyal to the brand of her youth. It had served her well and the assistant behind the Elizabethan Arden counter knew Mrs Beaumont as a regular customer and had hopes of gathering in Amelia one of these days. Amelia went for cheaper lines, and today, while the two jars of cream were being popped into a bag, Mell took an eye shadow and a lipstick from a rotating display and said, 'These too, please.'

Then she went back to her van, parked in the yard behind the shop, tissued away the residue of the greyish-blue eye shadow she had always used, and applied the new with the aid of the little mirror stuck on the windscreen sunshield.

It was green, flecked with gold, and it seemed to bring out an amber light in eyes she had always thought were greyish blue. Then she put on the lipstick. She had been wearing a pale pink, she always did; this one was nearer the colour of the poppies, emphasing the soft fullness of her mouth. Finally she dabbed two spots of colour on her cheekbones, smoothing them with her fingertips.

She looked healthier and happier. She had three-quarters of an hour left of her lunch hour, less than ten minutes to the Angler's Arms and ten minutes back, and as soon as she got out of town and on to a straight road she put her foot down.

She hadn't been in this inn before. 'Good pub food', promised the notice, set to lure motorists into the car park which was almost full. She saw Barney's car and got out of her own, and the hot mid-day sun streamed around her. She reached for her straw hat on the passenger seat, but she hadn't worn it running round the shops and she would be going inside now.

It was a typical Cotswold pub, with low dark ceilings, the heavy beams studded with horse brasses. In cold weather, logs would burn in the big inglenook fireplace, but now there was an arrangement of beige teasels and silver honesty leaves, and copper kettles and pans set out in gleaming order.

The bar was standing room only, but she stood out in this crowd. Not dramatically, but today was different because she felt that the men who glanced her way when she walked in were aware of her. Usually glances passed over her but today she caught attention and when somebody asked, 'Looking for someone?' she smiled and said,

'Yes, and I've found him,' and somebody else chortled, 'Not your day, Charlie.'

Barney stood out in the crush, too. He was standing over by a window, conspicuous because of his height and the shock of black hair, and because most of those around him seemed to be looking at him. He signalled, but she had seen him and she shouldered her way towards him. As he came to meet her she thought, my heart's racing like a girl with her first crush. I missed this in my teens and now I'm old enough to recognise it as something terrific but temporary and I am going to enjoy every minute of it.

When she reached him he put an arm around her, getting her through the crowd, and it seemed natural that he should. And that when they arrived at the table by the window, where two men sat with pints and plates before them, his hand should stay lightly on her shoulder while he introduced them to her. 'Frank and Jock, and this is Mell.'

Frank was a smallish man, with fair hair and moustache; Jock was bigger and balding. They were both wearing open-necked shirts and they both looked at Mell approvingly as she moved into the seat on the settle they were holding for her. 'I got you a salad and a white wine,' said Barney, sitting beside her.

'A prawn salad. Lovely! Are you all from the dig?'

Frank Simpson was an archaeological photographer and college lecturer, and Jock Reddie was a bank manager on his summer vacation, and an experienced amateur digger. 'What's happening?' she asked, and as she ate they told her about gridding the site and fencing it off to keep the cows out, about the plans and the preparations.

This Roman villa, spotted from the skies, was a surprise and a bonus. She was interested in what they were telling her. They were both excited at its discovery and she could understand why, and yet she was so conscious of Barney that she had to concentrate to stop their voices fading out.

Barney put in the occasional word but Frank and Jock did most of the talking. Most of the time she looked at the man who was speaking, usually Frank or Jock, but even then she could see Barney's face and hands and feel him close beside her.

She finished her salad and sipped her wine. The men's empty plates had been whisked away and Barney asked, 'Do you use this place?'

'It's the first time I've been here.'

'Then you must see the garden.'

She could see it by twisting round in her seat and looking through the window. There was a flagstoned patio with tables shaded by multi-coloured umbrellas. The tables were full and beyond was a lawn that needed rain, where other customers ate their pub food and drank their drinks, and children played under the trees. As a garden it wasn't much, but it was less crowded than the bar and she would have gone almost anywhere with Barney if it meant being nearly alone with him.

She said, 'I'd like that,' and drained her wine glass and left Frank and Jock debating whether they should battle their way to the bar to get another couple of pints.

Barney took her hand. She had walked hand in hand before, but never been so conscious of the strength of fingers that were locked with hers. As they strolled across the patio she squeezed his hand and smiled and without checking his pace he cupped her chin, turning her face, and brushed her lips. He was practised at the casual caress, and she managed to go on walking without stumbling, although a pulse fluttered madly in her throat.

She swallowed and said, 'I've been printing flights of blue birds all morning.'

They were watched as they walked across the grass, the tall dark man with his animal grace and the girl, sparkling with an inner glow. It would be nothing unusual for him, but it was for her. She had always been overshadowed. As a child she had never shrieked, 'Look at me,' hanging upside down from a bough or riding a bike no-hands. Girl and woman, she had been quiet and reserved, but today she was getting her first taste of carefree youth.

'Your own design?' he asked.

'They all are.' She swung the hand he held. She felt like dancing, like whirling round and round between the trees and the lunch-hour diners. 'Today the blue birds,' she said, 'tomorrow the clouds.'

The lawn rose to a slight ridge which sloped down to the bed of a brook that should have been bubbling down from the hills towards the river. This summer it was a sluggish trickle; you didn't need the stepping stones to the opposite bank.

Children were playing over there, climbing on a couple of great felled trees that had been bark-stripped into natural climbing frames, and Mell and Barney sat on the grass and she asked who else had arrived at the dig.

He gave names, descriptions, sketchy backgrounds. She had never heard of any of them before, from the director to the amateurs, but she could imagine them and she wanted to meet them. She said so and he asked, 'Will you come over tonight?'

'I'm not sure.' There could be some sort of scene waiting at home, she had better not make any arrangements.

'Can I fetch you?'

If he did there would be a scene. 'No,' she said. 'If I can come I will.'

'Fair enough.' His voice was lazy but there was a sensuousness in him, as he lounged on the grass, that was as powerful as if he had pulled her against him. She could feel the hardness and the warmth of him, although he was only looking at her.

'What were you doing in a Greek jail?' she asked.

'Sleeping off a hangover from the local hooch.'

'Been in many jails?'

'Not a lot.' He grinned and she laughed, and a young mother called, 'Tracey, Martin. Come on back here, we're off.'

Two children wailed, 'Aw, not yet,' above the hubbub of childish voices and the mother came over the brook repeating, 'Come *on*,' in rising frustration.

'I'd better be off, too,' said Mell, looking at her watch in surprise.

Barney's friends were waiting for him. They went towards his car and he went with Mell to hers, and kissed her cheek as she opened the door.

She got into the driving seat and watched him walking away and saw a girl looking enviously at her through the window of the adjacent car. This was another new experience for her, being with a man other women fantasised about. She would hate to get serious about a man like that because she certainly couldn't handle the competition.

She was twenty minutes late getting back to the shop and Pammie, whose temper had not been improved by a crispbread lunch, was sulking. 'I thought you'd decided to take the afternoon off,' she said.

'Sorry,' said Mell and went downstairs to finish the blue bird roll, but when she heard the phone ringing unanswered she came up again. The shop was empty and she picked up the phone. 'Rainbow's End, can I help you?'

It was Nanny, checking that she would be home for a meal after work. She always was and she said, 'Yes, why?'

'I thought you might be going off with your new friend,' said Nanny.

'Not tonight.' Mell put down the phone as Pammie came back carrying a paper bag.

'Just popped next door to get a couple of buns, I'm starving,' said Pammie. She smiled sheepishly then giggled. 'There's a smashing American tourist in the cake shop. I told him I thought he was Ryan O'Neal.' She stood by the glass panel of the door, keeping watch. 'When he comes out I'm going to go out as if I've been arranging the window. I'll ask him what he thinks of it, that'll get him talking.'

'Drag him in and sell him a tie,' Mell joked.

She wished she hadn't promised to go straight home. She could have gone over to Ruddington and met some of the team and had a meal with Barney, because that was what she would like to do with her evenings while the dig was on.

Another thing she wanted was a new wardrobe, and she draped two dresses and a bright pink shirt over her arm as Pammie said, 'Oh hell, there's a girl with him.' She sounded quite outraged. 'I never noticed her.'

'Never mind,' said Mell, lips twitching as Pammie turned disconsolately from the window. 'There's lots more tourists in town.'

'Yeah,' said Pammie, brightening and diving into her bag of buns . . .

It was a humid evening when Mell came out of the

shop, just after six, and she could have done without Nanny's scolding and her mother's disapproval tonight. She drove home reluctantly, because all her instincts were to turn the van in another direction.

Watty had gone. The garden was empty and the house was quiet. Nanny was in the kitchen, occupied with the meal that she would serve at half past six. 'I thought some nice plaice,' she said. 'Grilled, with a butter and lemon sauce. You could do the salads for me.'

Mell swilled her hands at the sink. She would have liked a shower. Even the heat of the grill was enough to make the kitchen seem stifling. She opened the fridge door and took out salad stuffs. 'Your mother came back from the hairdressers with a headache,' said Nanny accusingly as Mell washed the lettuce and shook it in a drainer,

'Don't tell me, somebody told her about Barney,' said Mell.

Nanny's expression was grim. 'I thought you said there was nothing to tell.'

'Not yet,' Mell confirmed. 'Did you tell her?'

'No, I didn't.' Nanny changed from scolding to almost pleading. 'But she's going to hear and she shouldn't be worried like this, about you spoiling your chances of such a good match.'

A marriage has been arranged, thought Mell. A good match, but nobody asked me and a bank account isn't the biggest thrill in the world. The touch and taste of a real man can do more for a girl.

Nanny would have called that shameless talk. 'I don't know what's come over you,' she said now. 'The table's laid, you can take in the dishes. Your mother's resting upstairs, you can tell her we're ready.'

This was obviously a slight headache, Elizabeth had not taken to her bed for the night, and when Mell looked round the door she was met by wide open eyes. 'I got your pills,' she said. 'The meal's ready, are you coming down?'

Elizabeth was lying on the counterpane, fully dressed.

Now she slipped into her shoes. 'Oh yes, I'm coming down,' she said. 'We have to talk.'

Elizabeth Beaumont was a talker and tonight she would have plenty to say. 'You're being very provoking,' she began, when they were all three seated round the table and she had taken her first mouthful of fish. 'Robert might not be willing to wait for you.'

'That's a risk I'll take.' Mell ate slowly, her appetite dulled, as her mother went on about the advantages of being Mrs Robert Gunnison and living in such a substantial house. She knew it well, she described it in loving detail, and Mell knew she was seeing herself established there when her daughter was titular mistress of the Grange.

Nobody's mentioning the master bedroom, Mell thought, with inner amusement. That would be my territory; and the idea of sharing it with Robert was so ridiculous that she smiled. Her mother pounced on the smile, asking what was funny? and Mell thought, I can't imagine Robert shirtless, let alone naked; and clenched her teeth to hold down hysterical laughter.

'I can see nothing to laugh at,' Elizabeth said stiffly when Mell remained silent. 'Robert's been so good to you, taking you about, introducing you to his friends. You won't get asked out much without Robert behind you.'

'I thought I might take up archaeology,' said Mell and Elizabeth's face went blank. 'They're excavating a Roman villa over at Ruddington,' Mell explained. 'You can see the pattern from the sky. I'm going to do some digging in my spare time.'

'And this is why you don't want Robert's ring?' Elizabeth sounded bewildered.

'No,' said Mell, 'I don't want his ring because I don't want to get married yet. I'm going to help with the dig because it will be something I've never done.'

Nanny snorted and they sat in silence, all eating slowly and not very much. Then Elizabeth said suddenly, 'I don't know what to tell him.'

'Tell him that's it's very kind——' Mell began.

'But you don't know your own mind,' Elizabeth finished tartly, and unfairly because Mell did know her own mind. Up till now nobody had thought she had one. 'He's coming round tonight,' said Elizabeth, 'and you'd better leave this to me. It will be less embarrassing if I suggest he waits a few more months before he produces the ring. By then you might have come to your senses. So long as you don't do anything to make him wonder if you're the right girl after all. He has very high standards. Any sort of scandal, any sort of gossip ...' She left the rest unsaid, meaning that Robert Gunnison would promptly opt out. 'So keep out of the way,' she ordered. 'Stay in your room and we'll say you're out.'

'I'll do better than that,' said Mell. 'I'll go out.'

She left the house and got into the van, and she knew that while she was driving off Nanny would be telling her mother, very gently, about this man who was working up at this dig.

She drew up along the road to wind down the windows because she was stifling in the van, she could hardly breathe. And then she drove fast creating a current of air, and started to smile again, remembering Barney brushing the tangles out of her hair last night.

She felt as though she was escaping from prison, belting along in a getaway car, and whatever was waiting for her when she arrived where Barney was, she couldn't get to him fast enough.

CHAPTER FOUR

THERE were cars and motor bikes parked in the farmyard tonight, and sounds of music and voices came from the black barn. The doors were open and Mell lined up her van and walked across.

A long trestle table ran down the middle of the barn, which at first sight seemed to be crowded. Some sat on the benches at the table, where there was food and a radio. Others were standing around. Mell could see a couple of women through the rails of a loft up there.

She couldn't see Barney and she explained to the nearest man, thin and bearded in jeans and T-shirt, 'I'm looking for Barney.'

'Who isn't?' said the young man. 'A volunteer are you?'

She smiled. 'Not signed up yet. Do you know where I can find him?'

'Try the boathouse. Do you know where that is?'

'Yes,' she said. 'Thanks.'

Sheep were still grazing in the first field. There was no one about out here. Over the river in the field of the dig there was a white caravan and a large tent, and the chalked out pattern of the villa was fenced and pegged with cords into squares.

There was still not a breath of air; it was going to be another sultry night. She passed the weir where water foamed down. Beyond she could see the boat still moored under the willows and just up the little slipway, backed by the copse of trees, the boathouse. She climbed the wooden steps. The door at the top was ajar and she tapped and called, 'Hello,' and the door swung wider, but nobody answered.

She knew as soon as she stepped in that the flat was empty. He might have decided she wasn't coming and

she could either stay here and wait or go back to the
barn and ask if anyone else had any idea where she
might find him. She wasn't going home yet. Nobody
wanted her there for the next hour or two.

Back on the towpath she shouted, 'Barney,' and
jumped when this time he answered, because she
couldn't see him. 'Here,' he called. He was in the river,
waving a gleaming arm from which the water dripped,
hair black and smooth as a seal. 'Can you swim?'

'Of course.' She was a stylish swimmer, going quietly
through the water and rarely making waves.

'Come on in then.' She had only swum in swimming
pools and from warm safe holiday beaches but she was
hot and sticky now and it looked cool in the dark silver
water. She slipped off shoes, skirt and top, put her car
keys and watch in the toe of her shoe, and picked her
way to the river's edge in skimpy bra and pants,
laughing and feeling daring and devil-may-care.

Lordy she was pale! She knew she was pale but if the
heatwave went on she might try for a hint of a tan
before winter came. The water flowed by but it might
not be deep enough to dive and she slid down from the
bank. Her feet touched bottom and she began to swim
at once because it was surprisingly cold, striking
through the warmth of her skin and freezing her blood.

Barney was floating with no apparent effort but she
swam jerkily because the icy shock had tightened up her
muscles. 'It's c-cold,' she spluttered, and then, 'I'll
warm up in a minute.'

'Sure you will.' His teeth flashed white in the dark
face. 'You are all right?'

'Fine.' Now she was in she wanted to show him what
she could do. She blinked the water out of her eyes and
tossed back her streaming hair. There was something
else that was different about this water: the currents,
tugging and nudging her. It was nothing to be scared of
but she didn't think she would risk river swimming on
her own.

'I'm glad you came,' he said.

'So am I.' It was more exhilarating than a swimming pool, and very soon she was warm and swimming a leisured crawl, keeping pace with him although she supposed he might be adjusting his stroke to hers. Either way they were swimming along together, an arm's distance apart, and the river and the man were both new and strange and exciting and she said, 'This is the place to be on a night like this. I wonder they're not all in the river.'

'Nobody's thought of it yet.'

'Do you swim often?'

'Most nights.'

'How long have you been here?'

'On and off just under a month. I came down as soon as Alan told me they'd spotted a villa and his old man gave the go-ahead for a dig. Since then I've been getting a team together.'

'They're all your friends?'

'Most of them I've worked with. This is a rush job, he doesn't want a permanent excavation in his field, but it might be rewarding.'

She had fallen back a little so that she was swimming behind him, watching the bronzed rippling back and shoulders, the rise and fall of the arms. Very nice, she thought, you swim very nicely, I bet you could go on for miles and I'll have to be the one to suggest we turn back.

'By the way,' she asked, 'what's your surname?'

'Rudd.'

'Barnaby Rudd.' She frowned over that and then realised it reminded her of Charles Dickens's *Barnaby Rudge* and joked, 'I thought for a minute that I knew your family.' He didn't answer. *'Barnaby Rudge.'*

'The village idiot.'

'Was he?' She had read the book long ago, she could hardly remember the plot. 'I suppose he was. Another Barnaby. No, I don't know your family. Sorry.'

'Don't apologise,' he said, 'I don't know yours.' Nor would he if she could help it.

He swam on, increasing the gap between them, and as she opened her mouth to shout, 'Wait for me,' a current caught her, sucking suddenly so that she went under, mouth and nose filling with water. That would have been nothing, but her kicking foot encountered something that was festooned with weeds. The water stung where she had drawn it into her lungs and the weeds were holding her, and she panicked, writhing and fighting in choking and mindless confusion.

She didn't see Barney—it was dark under water—but she felt the weeds being pulled away and her arm seized, and then floating up and coughing and retching when her head broke the surface.

She had been terrified. She couldn't get out a word until he hauled her out of the river and she was huddled on the bank. Then he asked, 'Was it cramp?' She nearly said yes. She was rubbing her legs but that was nervous reaction. The only reason she had been helpless was because she had lost her head, and now she hiccuped, 'I never swam in a river before. It was the first time anything's grabbed me underwater and it's dark down there, even if it isn't very deep.'

'Another kick and you'd have freed yourself,' he said. 'It was weed around the root of a tree.'

Maybe she would have twisted free even if she had gone on panicking but she said, 'Thank goodness you were here.'

'Any time,' he said and she thought, no, not any time. Nothing about this is for ever.

She was shivering, rubbing her arms now, but when he sat down beside her and took her hands she felt strength flowing into her again, and even managed a small smile. 'I wonder if they swam in the river from the villa.'

'Probably,' he said. 'Villas were usually built by running water. There's a circle marking what was more than likely the site of a shrine, possibly a water deity, a nymph or something along those lines.'

'Could be the one who grabbed me. Did they go in for sacrifice?'

'You wouldn't be the sacrifice. You'd be the water nymph.'

She hadn't felt much like a water nymph just now but she wouldn't panic again. It had been the un-expectedness of it that threw her. 'I keep seeing you as the barbarian,' she said. 'What do you think happened to the nymphs when the barbarians arrived?'

He kissed her, pressing her back in the dry brittle grass, and her lips curved under his mouth. 'Very likely,' she said, but this was no place for more than a kiss although she was not sure she could have stopped if he hadn't. Hearing voices was almost a relief.

She sat up and looked for intruders and they waved from the opposite bank, three of them in jeans and shirts, and after the first glance she was so appalled by her own appearance that she couldn't have said if they were men or girls because she was frantically trying to cover herself up. The white nylon, clinging to her wet skin, was so transparent that all was revealed. 'I must get my clothes on,' she yelped and Barney grinned. 'Sorry, but I can't offer you anything. I need all the covering I've got.'

His swimming briefs were brief and she said, 'I can see that,' shaken with laughter. But they would be swimming against the river going back and she was not sure she could make it. She said, 'I could stick on a few leaves because I think I'll be walking.'

'I'll fetch your clothes for you.' But there were gnats about and there was a lot of her exposed. One settled on her arm and she flicked it off.

'Let's run,' she said, but that had its snags. The ground was rock hard, liberally laced with sharp stones, and she was wincing and hopping almost at once. 'Would you fetch them?' she had to ask. 'While I hide in the trees.'

'Come on,' he said, 'I'll carry you.'

He scooped her up as he spoke as easily as if she was a child, and she gasped, 'Hang on,' but he was striding on, no trouble at all, and she had to put her arms round his neck. And she had to smile, because he did.

A memory stirred, of being carried to bed as a child in her father's arms, feeling safe and sleepy. She had no clear memories of her father. The turmoil that followed his death had almost blotted out her early years, and now she said to Barney, 'Tell me about your mother and father.'

'Why?'

She had her head against his chest so that she didn't see his face but when he spoke, even just one word, she could feel the sound of it inside him. And his heartbeats, slow and deep, if she moved a little. 'I wondered what they were like,' she said and he laughed and she listened to the laughter through his skin.

'So did I,' he said, 'but not for a long time.'

As she realised what that meant she began to stammer apologies, but he sounded cheerful about it.

'Worse things happen. From what I'm told families can be a mixed blessing. What are yours like?'

'My father died when I was five. My mother's very beautiful.'

'Of course.'

'Not like me. She doesn't look like me at all.'

'That must be a trial to her,' he said, and she threw back her head to laugh so that her wet hair tickled her back.

'I'm a trial right now,' she said. 'But not because she'd like to look like me.'

'Why?'

'Like you say, families bring problems. My mother wants me to settle down with somebody she considers suitable.'

Another little group was strolling on the opposite bank, calling across, 'What's going on then?'

'Just giving a lady a lift,' Barney called back, and Mell waved graciously, doing a take-off of royalty through a limousine window. He showed no sign of tiring and when they reached her pile of clothes she was quite sorry to be set down.

She tipped out the watch and keys and got into the shoes, picking up skirt and shirt, and he asked, 'He's your mother's choice, not yours?'

'Not mine yet, at any rate.' By the time winter came she might have run her course of summer madness. This could be a brief rebellion. In the end she could find herself wearing Robert's mother's ring.

He tucked a long strand of wet hair behind her ear. 'Don't let anybody push you,' he said.

She was almost sure she wouldn't. 'I won't,' she said. 'May I wash down in your bathroom?' She had better wash her hair, too, before she went home, and she scurried up the wooden staircase as Barney stopped to speak to a man with a dog who was walking towards them down the towpath.

The door was still ajar but this time the flat was not empty. A girl was sitting, feet up on the sofa. She was very slim, wearing a white sleeveless dress, and there were white pumps beside the settee. Lips, toenails and fingernails were painted coral, matching coral earrings and necklace. Her hair was dark red, drawn back in a thick plait almost to her waist. She had small regular features and the blue unblinking stare of a Siamese cat.

'Looking for someone?' she said.

Mell clutched her clothes and stammered, 'We've— been swimming.'

'I wondered why you were undressed.' Barney's voice and the man's drifted up. 'I'm Gemma Carrington,' said the girl as though that should mean something, and Mell said,

'Amelia Beaumont,' before she remembered her new name. 'Excuse me,' she went on, 'while I get into something more comfortable.' She edged her way round into the bathroom and the girl watched her in a rather weary fashion.

In the bathroom Mell put her clothes on the stool and sat on the edge of the bath. Somebody waiting for Barney. Somebody sensational and sure of herself. And no surprise at all, because he was a dangerously desirable man. But she must guard against jealousy.

She peeled off her bra and pants that were still sticking to her. They were river tacky and for all the cover they'd given she might as well have taken everything off before she went into the water. Now she swilled them through and rolled them tightly in a towel to squeeze out as much moisture as possible. She washed herself quickly and swished her hair under a running tap, although as the water was cold and there was no shampoo her hair didn't look much better for it.

When she unrolled the towel her undies were still uncomfortably damp. If Gemma had not been out there she might have asked Barney if he had anything that could substitute for underwear. Glamour was immaterial. But she couldn't face Gemma while she requested the loan of a vest and a Y-front, so she settled for putting on her pants and rolling her bra into a small handful.

Barney was wearing a short, navy blue towelling robe, talking though the open door of the bedroom. Gemma was still on the sofa and as Mell walked back into the living room she began laughing at something he had just said.

Mell smiled uncertainly. She was sure they were not laughing at her but Gemma's smile was mocking, taking in Mell's damp and shiny look.

'All through?' Barney asked.

'Yes thanks.'

He made for the bathroom, carrying clothes, and Gemma said, 'I've been sent to collect him. We're going out for a meal. The director, Professor Arnold Richmond no less, and some of the others. I suppose you don't feel like coming along?'

'Of course she does,' said Barney. 'I'll only be a couple of minutes.'

'Well,' said Gemma when the bathroom door closed, 'do you?'

Not looking this way. Besides, Mell thought with an

inward giggle, if I sit down my skirt will stick to my bottom. She said, 'I've eaten, and I think I'd like to get home to my own bathroom, but I'll be back tomorrow. I'll come in the afternoon and do some work.'

'We can always use another worker,' said Gemma sweetly. 'Have you had any experience?'

'No.'

'I didn't think you had.' That had a double meaning the way she said it, although she went on, 'We'll team you with someone who has,' and Mell asked,

'Are you an archaeologist?'

Gemma smiled towards the bathroom door. 'I'm here for the digger rather than the dig.'

She was putting Mell down and she would be easier to deal with when Mell looked less of a slob. 'Really?' said Mell. 'Well, I'll see you tomorrow,' and she smiled and went.

She got into her van and had the key in the ignition when the bearded lad tapped on the window. She wound it down and he asked, 'Did you find Barney?'

'Yes.'

'Did Gemma find you?' He was noting her wet hair. 'She didn't push you into the river?'

'Does she do that kind of thing?'

He grinned. 'She'd like to, if she dared.'

'We went swimming,' said Mell.

'Well,' he said, 'don't let her see you off. You'll be coming back?'

'Tomorrow afternoon.'

'See you then.'

I wonder if he's experienced, she thought. I wonder if I'll get paired with him. If Gemma's here I'll be lucky if I end up with Barney.

Robert's car was still outside the house and she opened the back door quietly. The kitchen door was shut and she tiptoed past, into the dining-room-cum-hall towards the stairs. The lounge door was open. She was framed in it briefly, but long enough for Robert to say, 'Good evening, Amelia.'

'Hallo,' she carolled back and her mother said wearily,

'Oh, come in.'

She almost pretended not to hear, which would have been childish, but she stuffed the bra under a cushion before she joined them. Her apperance was going to be shock enough without carrying her underwear in with her, and they both goggled as if she was wearing a horror mask.

Her mother turned to stare at the window pane, checking for a sudden cloudburst, and then gasped, 'What happened to you?'

'I went swimming.'

'You what? Where?'

'In the river. I went to the dig. It's by the river. They're a cheery crowd.'

Robert glowered. He found the idea of his ladylike Amelia splashing around in the river highly distasteful. And who were this cheery crowd? Elizabeth had just confessed that she had told Amelia about the ring and Amelia had been overwhelmed and perhaps Robert should give her a little more time to get used to the idea of marriage. Dear Robert had so much to offer that Amelia was slightly in awe of such a glittering prize although, as her mother, Elizabeth knew she was a very sensible girl and a little shyness these days was refreshing, wasn't it?

He had not been too disappointed, he approved of shyness in women, but now he was wondering whether Amelia could be getting into bad company. Swimming in the river at night—and dusk was falling—with a cheery crowd, seemed quite out of character.

'The *river*?' Elizabeth wailed. 'But that's dangerous. You could catch all manner of things.' She meant some dread disease, but Mell thought, I could have drowned in the water and been seduced on the bank, so you are right, it was dangerous, and she couldn't help smiling.

'Excuse me,' she said, 'I'd better fix my hair.'

Upstairs she shot into the bathroom, showered and washed her hair, and she was in her bedroom, in dressing-gown, blowing her hair dry when Nanny walked in. 'What's this?' demanded Nanny. 'This' was Mell's bra. She couldn't have covered it completely with the cushion.

'I went swimming,' said Mell.

'I know you went swimming. Your mother came into the kitchen to get the coffee; she told me. What I want to know is, what did you go swimming in?'

Mell opened wide bland eyes. 'The river,' she said.

'Don't get cheeky with me, young lady.' The old woman was quivering with indignation. 'You get dressed and come down. Your mother's trying to explain about this dig, whatever it is.'

'Don't worry,' said Mell. 'An archaeological excavation is a very respectable set-up.'

'Is it?' shrilled Nanny. 'But it wasn't an archaeological anything you went over to see tonight, was it? It was this gypsy feller. I wasn't born yesterday.'

Mell finished drying her hair, more or less, dressed and went down into the lounge, where her mother and Robert had the Spode coffee cups and the silver coffee set on the small Regency sofa-table. And two cut-glass brandy glasses.

Elizabeth smiled across at her daughter with spurious gaiety. 'Ah, there you are, darling, come and tell us about this—Roman villa, isn't it?'

Mell hadn't bothered with make-up. She wore the first dress she had grabbed from her wardrobe, which was a plain white shift, and she hadn't waited for her hair to dry completely. It fell smoothly around her smooth face and yet when she walked into the room and sat down both of them were aware of a change in her. Something inside, an inner excitement.

Elizabeth could not remember ever sitting silent and listening to her daughter, but now she listened because she was, for the moment, at a loss for words. She had forgotten the aerial spotting of the villa; Robert recalled it, although until tonight he had not realised that anything was being done about it. But Mell told them about the colony of experts and helpers who had arrived, the plan of the villa that had been marked out, what the rooms might have been. Her enthusiasm made everything vivid. She talked with shining eyes and a new confidence.

'But it won't be there now, will it?' said Elizabeth. 'Surely there'll be nothing there now. These are just foundation marks.'

'Who knows?' said Mell. 'Anything would be thrilling to see after all these years. And the villas always had mosaic floors and elaborate bath-houses, so we might unearth some ancient plumbing.'

They both noticed that she said 'we', not 'they'. 'Somebody's been giving you a history lesson,' said Robert, and Elizabeth thought, and that's not the only lesson. Mell read their thoughts and watched Elizabeth pick up the brandy glass and knew this was to hide annoyance and look composed.

'I wonder how you'll find the time,' said Robert. 'I hope this doesn't mean you'll be deserting old friends.' He sounded jovial but Mell knew that he must have sat behind his desk many a time, listening to clients and looking like this.

She said, 'I thought I might take tomorrow afternoon off.'

'Shutting the shop?' Thursday was half-day. Tomorrow was Tuesday. Elizabeth disliked changes in routine, and besides the shop brought in good money.

'Pammie can manage,' said Mell.

'I was hoping you'd have dinner with me tomorrow night,' said Robert. 'But you seem to have made prior arrangements.'

He expected her to say she would be back home in the evening and would be available around their usual time. When she said, 'Well yes, I have,' he felt more rebuffed than when Elizabeth had advised him to delay offering Amelia an engagement ring.

Elizabeth said hastily, 'Wednesday. You come to us Wednesday and Nanny will cook something special.' But Nanny's cooking and Elizabeth's smile couldn't dispel his unease. He had seen marriages go wrong when the man had chosen a much younger wife. He had never considered Amelia's youth, she had always seemed so quiet and sensible, but perhaps he should start thinking about it.

'I'm not sure I can make Wednesday,' he said and, hardly drawing breath, 'and I should be saying good night. I am expecting a phone call. Business you know.'

His coffee cup was half full and he hadn't finished his brandy. Mell expected her mother to point that out, and coax him into staying until he had promised to come back on Wednesday night, but Elizabeth got up, too, and said sweetly, 'Of course you must be there for your phone call. I'll see you out.' She went with him. Mell heard her calling gaily, 'Drive carefully now,' from the front door. Then the door closed and there was silence in the house.

She had a mental picture of her mother leaning against the door, eyes closed, fighting for composure, because she had no doubt that Elizabeth was furious, and when she reappeared there were two bright spots of colour in her cheekbones. No wonder she let Robert go, Mell thought, it must have been hard for her to keep smiling when she was dying to throw something at the wall, preferably me.

Elizabeth walked across the room without a word, sat down again on the chaise longue, and picked up a brandy glass. She held it in shaking hands, turning it as if she was looking for flaws, and Mell thought, good grief, she *is* wondering whether to throw it.

'Smashing that would only make you madder,' she said, and her mother put the glass down again and said, 'Don't be ridiculous. Who is he?'

Mell said, 'I suppose you mean the man I met at the boot fair?'

'The one you went out to meet last night when you pretended to have a headache.'

'I didn't go out to meet anyone. I went to the shop to unload the van and met him by accident and he took me to see the dig.'

'Who *is* he?' Elizabeth's voice was rising.

'He's an archaeologist.' Mell didn't say, 'He has no family and he doesn't know who his parents were. I doubt if he has money in the bank but he'll never go hungry because he is a very tough customer.' She did say, 'I'd made up my mind I couldn't take Robert's ring days ago. The villa is just something I'll enjoy helping in, and I hope to make some new friends, but——'

'When I think what Robert was offering you,' Elizabeth wailed, 'and you're throwing it all away. And you are throwing it away, because Robert's going to hear about this man and Nanny says he's a gypsy.'

Mell knew she shouldn't laugh but she couldn't help it. 'That's Hilda Hallchurch, because he's got black hair and when she saw him he wasn't wearing a shirt.'

'Half naked.' Elizabeth shuddered, and Mell bit back another yelp of laughter, because this was ridiculous.

'Fortunately,' she said, 'it was the half that didn't matter.'

She didn't mean to tease, although that kind of remark would not have gone down well with her mother at any time, and now it sent Elizabeth out of control. She sat there spitting fury, her usually unlined face clenched into angry furrows and her hands two small flailing fists. She told Mell what a ninny she was, what a reputation she would be getting. All the tongues would be wagging, everybody would be sniggering, and at the end of it he wouldn't want her.

Robert wouldn't, Robert wouldn't be back, Elizabeth was not talking about Robert. She meant the gypsy. 'In six months time,' Elizabeth shrieked, 'you'll have nothing, *nothing!*'

Chill struck Mell, like the cold of the river, stopping her breath as she was seized by a premonition of something terrible. She saw her mother still mouthing but she couldn't hear the words. She was frozen as though she was lost and alone and the world was ending in an ice age.

She almost screamed herself. Then Nanny came rushing in and Mell clasped her head between her hands and huddled down in her chair and Nanny had her arms around Elizabeth and was crooning, 'Hush now, hush.'

Mell should not have let it come to this. Her mother must not be upset. That must be what had struck Mell, guilt and fear that she might have put too much strain on the heart that murmured. Elizabeth was pale again now, smooth faced as though the anger had washed through her.

'Oh, you're a selfish girl,' Nanny scolded, as Mell went to kneel beside Elizabeth begging, 'Please Mother, don't cry, don't make yourself ill,' and put a hand on her arm that Nanny looked in two minds about knocking off.

Mell and Nanny both waited apprehensively because Elizabeth had had heart trouble at less dramatic moments, but now she sat very still, her eyes wide as though she had frightened herself. And when Nanny asked, 'Do you want a pill?' she shook her head and whispered, 'I'm all right.'

'No thanks to some,' said Nanny, glaring at Mell, and then, turning on her favourite child, 'And no thanks to you either, getting yourself into this state. I heard you from the kitchen.'

'I lost my temper,' said Elizabeth meekly. 'This has been such a disappointment. I'm terribly unhappy.' Tears were still on her cheeks and Mell suggested,

'Do you want to lie down?'

'I shall have a cup of tea,' said Elizabeth, 'and play some music.' She dabbed her eyes with a lace-edged handkerchief and went over to the piano and began to play a sad little melody. Mell went into the kitchen to make the tea.

That was the worst scene she could remember. Her mother had always had tantrums from time to time and heart pills were always at the ready, but Mell could never remember her screaming before. This upset to her carefully laid plans had been a real blow to her and it had certainly frightened Mell. For a few moments in there she had felt as if her own heart would stop beating.

Elizabeth kept up her playing for over an hour. Nanny read a large-print thriller in the lounge, listening to the music, and Mell stayed in the kitchen and made sketches for a design that she would later carve in wooden blocks. A water theme might be fun: seahorses, starfish, trailing weed.

The weed around her ankle had been terrifying. She would never forget the blessed feeling of release and escape and being able to breathe again. Barney had saved her just as he had at the drag-racing, although he said he hadn't, but she must not rely on him for too much. Her mother was right when she said six months was the longest Mell would have. Less in fact, not much more than three. But Mell would not be left with nothing, because there would be memories, some laughs, some happy times, maybe discoveries where the villa used to be.

She had doodled as she thought about other things and when she glanced down several of the squiggles were hearts. She wrote 'B' in the largest and smiled and pushed that page aside and went back to her design.

She was amusing herself with a fat fish when her mother came into the kitchen. The music had calmed Elizabeth. She looked herself again, but with a long-suffering air. 'Good night,' she said, 'I'm going to bed.'

'Good night,' said Mell. 'Shall I bring you——?'

'No thank you.' Elizabeth touched her temples lightly, with her fingertips. 'I couldn't touch a thing. I shall try to sleep, but it won't be easy.'

She glanced over the papers on the table, without much interest until she spotted the heart with 'B' in it and then she sighed deeply and went without another word. Mell screwed up the page and dropped it into the waste bin before Nanny came in. Nanny arrived within the minute and Mell begged, 'Don't start.'

'I've said all I'm going to say.' But her expression
spoke volumes and Mell thought, I should be so lucky.

She said, 'It didn't take much to see Robert off.
When I said I couldn't have dinner with him tomorrow
he remembered he was expecting a phone call and had
to get home right now. And he doesn't want to come to
a meal here on Wednesday either, thanks all the same,
so that was hardly a deathless devotion.'

The old woman's lips parted, then closed because she
could not deny that Robert Gunnison had not shown
much fighting spirit . . .

Mell slept soundly. She thought she might have
dreamed because she woke feeling warm and wonderful
and, still half asleep, stretched out a hand to touch the
pillow. I had a good night, she thought, and got up smiling
at herself. These days there seemed more to smile at,
although Nanny was still glum in the kitchen and it was
doubtful if Watty would get many mugs of tea today.

Pammie was on time this morning, and while Mell
was saying, 'Morning,' Pammie was asking, 'Come on,
what's been happening? Did you see him last night?'

'I went over to the dig,' said Mell. 'I'm taking the
afternoon off, you can manage, can't you?'

'By myself you mean?' Pammie pulled a face. 'Oh I
don't know about that.'

Pammie took afternoons off, days off, and Mell had
never been rushed off her feet. 'Of course you can
manage,' said Mell. 'You do all the time while I'm
downstairs.'

Just before one she changed into a pair of bright blue
shorts, and a blue cheesecloth shirt which she knotted
under her breasts. It was another scorching day and
digging would be sweating work, but she applied plenty
of suntan cream and wondered how Gemma would be
dressed, and whether she wore gloves to prevent that
coral nail varnish chipping. Perhaps she didn't dig.
Perhaps she sat on a grassy bank peeling grapes and
looking sexy.

Pammie was sitting behind the desk, eating an apple, and when Mell came up the stairs she looked enviously at the bare flat midriff and the long slim legs. Until now she had hardly realised that Mell had legs. 'Won't you burn?' she asked.

'I'm covered in sun cream.'

'So you are.' Pammie could see the sheen of it. 'If he tries to get a grip on you you'll shoot through his fingers!'

I'm more likely to burst into flames, thought Mell, and she laughed. 'Depends on how good the grip is.'

Lunch hour was almost over when Mell reached the farm. As she got out of her van the bearded man came over, paper cup in one hand, sandwich in the other. 'I've been watching for you,' he announced and identified himself. 'I'm Jim McKie, reading archaeology at Southampton.'

'I'm Mell Beaumont,' she said, 'selling clothes in Long Campden.'

'Barney's in the van. He said to tell you when you came.'

She didn't ask about Gemma. She thanked Jim, who fell into step beside her through the field where the sheep grazed and told her that probes had hit bedrock which could be a floor in the main room. They were concentrating there and on one other room. At the moment there was a team of fifteen, which was pretty damn good. Barney had gathered them in. Jim had had his summer vacation mapped out when Barney had rung him and said there was this villa, and he had jacked in a trip to the Himalayas to come here.

This was the first time Mell had seen cows in the field. They must be in the milking sheds at night. Now there was a herd of black and white Friesians held back by the fencing around the gridded area, but skirting it, putting their heads over, as if this was their territory and they were suspicious of intruders.

Jim pointed towards the small white caravan pitched under a horse chestnut tree and said, 'Barney's in there.'

CHAPTER FIVE

THE barn was blissfully cool after the long hot afternoon. At half past six the diggers downed tools and labouring work was over for the day. Barney was chatting with Frank and the grey-haired woman, over by the circle of the little shrine, and Mell went along with the crowd of young folk who were heading for a wash and a meal.

They had the use of the wash-house in the farmyard but she joined the queue for the pump. She was suddenly exhausted. She hadn't realised she was so out of condition but her head was starting to spin. It was help-yourself in an outhouse: salad, beefburgers, sausages and beans, and the sight and smell of food made her queasy. She took a glass of lemonade and then walked over to the barn with a girl called Sylvia, who was an art student here with her boyfriend.

Sylvia was a bright, fizzy little redhead. They were all bright, it seemed to Mell, and all set to make an evening of it. The older men and women were booked into hotels and bed and breakfasts, but the young ones were living in the barn, sleeping on camp beds and in sleeping bags, men on the ground floor, girls in the loft.

Barney hadn't appeared yet, he had probably gone along to the boathouse; and there was no sign of Gemma, who was more than likely there already; and Mell thought, I am going home, I don't feel so good. Somebody was strumming a guitar, and it went through her head like the drums of a steel band.

It was cool in the barn but she seemed to be running a temperature and she told Jim, 'I have to go, I've got a date. I'll be back Thursday afternoon, that's my half-day closing,' and she hurried out to the van feeling hotter by the moment. She hadn't just caught the sun, she had been clobbered by it. Her skin was burning and her head was bursting, and if the distance between here and home had been any further she would have had to beg a lift. As it was when she drew up in the drive she almost collapsed over the wheel. Then she made a dive for the house and the bathroom and was violently sick.

Nanny had followed her up the stairs and when Mell raised a scarlet face from the loo basin Nanny shrieked, 'What have you done to yourself?'

'Too much sun.' Mell's teeth chattered although she was on fire. 'I feel rotten.'

Nanny was torn between sympathy and censure. She was fussing and scolding all the time. 'Oh, you poor lamb! Oh, you *silly* girl! Oh, you never sat out in the sun with only this on!' And when Mel took off her shirt and shorts every unprotected inch was bright red: arms, legs, midriff, face.

She hadn't even worn her hat. She must have been crazy. Most folk had grown accustomed to the sun this summer but until today she had hidden from it, and then she had imagined that a coating of cream would protect her. She felt as if she had been dropped into boiling water and hauled out scalded and smarting unbearably. Added to which her innards were churning.

Nanny produced calamine and a swab of cotton wool and dabbed away. It cooled for the moment where it touched, and left her grotesquely white and scarlet, but that was the least of her worries. She could hardly bear even a sheet over her. It hurt to move; it hurt to lie still, she could have sworn she was on fire. But it was worse when she had to keep rushing to the bathroom.

Mell had had no illnesses except the usual childhood complaints but it had always been Nanny who nursed her. Elizabeth had drifted into the sickroom, so long as it was nothing contagious, but Nanny had fetched and carried and dosed and comforted. While Mell was sipping her third glass of fruit juice now Nanny said, 'Your mother's out,' and Mell croaked, 'Good.'

Elizabeth came in when she came back from her
evening with friends, and screeched at Mell's scarlet and
white face. 'You're going to be disfigured!'

'She's going to peel,' said Nanny balefully, and Mell
could well have burst into tears if she hadn't had to
jump out of bed at that moment and rush for the
bathroom.

It was a night of acute discomfort, and next morning
there was not a hope of her getting to the shop so she
went downstairs, barefoot in a cotton nightdress, to
ring Pammie's home. If her mother or Nanny had
passed on the message they would have had her at
death's door and Pammie liked a drama. Mell sat
awkwardly, keeping back and legs from the chair, and
said, 'You were right about yesterday, I did get burned.'

Pammie giggled. 'Was it worth it?'

'No it wasn't, you should see me. I feel rotten and I'll
have to shut the shop unless you can manage.'

Pammie said she might as well go along as she had
nothing else to do, and she hoped Mell would be all
right soon. 'You've got such a pale skin, haven't you,
and you've always worn sleeves and a big hat. Looks
like you're not meant to be stripping off.'

Elizabeth agreed. Mell spent the day in bed, sore
from head to foot, and her mother said she deserved it.

The doctor looked in and looked at her with raised
grizzled eyebrows. He had been treating Elizabeth
occasionally for years but this was the first time he had
been called to Mell since she had measles. 'We have
overdone it, haven't we?' he said.

'I didn't realise I was burning.' ... 'All right?'
Barney had asked her a couple of times. 'Fine,' she had
answered blithely, 'Fine' ... And now she looked like
overdone sizzling steak.

The doctor left a prescription for pills and lotions,
and instructions to Nanny to carry on with the glucose
drinks, and Nanny bustled around, her arthritis in
abeyance. Dabbing the parts Mell couldn't reach with
the cooling lotion, she said, 'I'm glad Robert can't see

you now. Any rate this ought to show you you're not up to this gypsy feller's shenanigans.'

'What are you talking about?'

'Well look at you. One afternoon up at this dig-place half kills you.'

'This isn't the digging. This is because I'm not used to the sun.'

'You're not used to a lot of things,' said Nanny darkly, corking the lotion while Mell eased herself round on the bed. 'And most of them are best left alone. You're a pretty picture now. It's doing you a lot of good, this carry-on.'

'Just let me smoulder in peace,' Mell begged.

Pammie came round that evening, and stood at the bottom of the bed and said, 'You *are* red.'

That was Mell's face, striped bright red on forehead, cheekbones and nose, against the white pillow. 'And the rest,' said Mell. 'Was it all right today?'

Pammie had managed. She had sold a few things, a commercial traveller had called and she had told him to come back next week. He had been fifty if he was a day and not dishy. 'How about tomorrow?' she asked. 'It's half-day isn't it? Shall we bother opening? I could use a morning off.'

Mell could do nothing. 'All right,' she said.

Pammie came round to get a closer look at her and declared, 'I've seen some bad sunburns this summer but I think you're the worst. You won't be digging again for a bit. You won't be seeing Barney looking like this, will you?'

'I'm going to make myself a veil,' said Mell. 'Something very oriental and romantic.' And Pammie almost believed her until she started to laugh. The laughter hurt her cheeks and thinking of Barney hurt too, remembering Gemma with her predatory eyes and that beautiful bronzed satin skin . . .

Thursday evening Mell came downstairs. After two days in bed her temperature was normal and she felt better, but now her skin was literally sloughing off, causing a piebald effect.

Her mother had gone out to play bridge. Thursday night was always bridge night, but she told Mell before she left that she was not looking forward to it. Wherever she went these days there were questions about Mell and Robert, and now Mell was down with heatstroke and they would be asking about that.

'That shouldn't be hard to explain,' said Mell wearily. 'This summer's been one long heatwave.'

Elizabeth, cool and elegant in a white linen suit, stood by the window fiddling with some roses that Watty had sent in from the garden. She pricked her finger and sucked it and said petulantly, 'If this had happened before you jilted Robert I'd have thought that too much sun had given you a brainstorm. That might have been some explanation.'

'Sorry I didn't time it better,' said Mell.

Nanny had just gone out of the house, too, to a WI meeting, when the phone rang and Mell wondered if it was Barney. He would have expected to see her this afternoon. When she didn't turn up he could have found her home number, there weren't that many Beaumonts in the book.

She hurried down and caught it before it stopped ringing. But it was a wrong number and disappointment struck her like a blow, she had been so sure she would hear his voice when she said, 'Hallo.' When it was a stranger asking for a stranger her face crumpled as she replaced the phone.

He probably hadn't missed her at all. Well he must have *missed* her, they'd all know she wasn't there. But with Gemma hovering in the wings and probably living in the boathouse, and all the dig team for company, why should he be in a hurry to track her down?

Depression was settling on her. She didn't want to go back to bed. She was light-headed and sore but she wasn't tired. Down here she could watch TV, make phone calls. She would have to ring Pammie if Pammie didn't ring her; she really couldn't see herself getting back to work before the weekend.

She went back upstairs, smoothed on more oil all over and slipped into a light cotton housecoat over her nightdress. She brought a bath towel down with her because if she got oil on the velvet and brocade of chairs and sofa her mother would never forgive her. Then she took an orange juice from the fridge and carried it into the lounge and picked up a magazine and leafed through it. It was full of beautiful women, every one of whom has had sense enough not to get burned by the sun.

The knock on the door almost made her spill her drink. It could be Barney. Highly unlikely but possible. It would be nice if he had bothered to find her and she couldn't resist checking.

She peeked from behind a curtain and it *was* his car parked in front of the house and she rushed for the door to let him in. Because of course she wanted to see him and she didn't care if she did look like a moth-eaten clown. She had her hand on the latch before the thought struck her, what if Gemma's with him? All the same she lifted the latch, and he was alone and all her gloom left her.

'What the hell?' he said.

'I got a bit sunburned.'

'You can say that again.'

'Come in.' She led the way into the lounge, suddenly and sharply conscious of everything: her flimsy clothing, her scarlet skin, most of all of Barney—of every inch of him—following behind her. 'I'm oily,' she said, and, because the towel was draped over the chaise longue, 'Take any other chair.' She sat down herself and he asked,

'This happened on Tuesday?'

'Yes.'

'You certainly copped it. How are you feeling?'

'Not bad now.'

'You're not the outdoor type, are you?' He drew up a chair close to her, looking at her with wry concern, radiating so much vitality that all the faded colours in the room seemed to brighten. She said again,

'It wasn't the digging, it was the sun. I've always taken it in very small doses, even on holidays abroad, but on Tuesday I didn't.'

He put a light cool hand on her forehead and she said quickly, 'I don't have a temperature.' Not any longer and she didn't want to sound too fragile. 'Next time I'll wear a hat,' she said. 'How are you doing? How's it going?'

'We're reaching walls. Finding pieces of masonry.'

'I'll be along again.' He looked doubtful and she said gaily, 'So I got sunburned, but it's only skin deep. I myself personally am strong as an ox.'

He laughed, but it was almost true, and sitting here now, sipping her iced orange juice, she was feeling healthier all the time. She offered a drink.

'Not right now thanks,' he said, and he described exactly what was being uncovered so that she could imagine the site two days on from how she had left it. He told her about the cow called Mabel who had taken a dislike or a liking—they weren't sure which—to one of the diggers, and who came galloping over every time David emerged from behind the barriers. Mabel had already sent him flying into the hedge and nearly into the river.

Mell remembered David. He had been playing the guitar in the barn when she was starting to feel like death. 'Everybody else all right?' she asked.

'Yes.' The others were used to the sun in open spaces. Mell was the novice, the newcomer; they had probably all known each other for ages. Even Gemma, who didn't dig, had been around nearly two years to Jim's knowledge. Mell said,

'Gemma is quite a number. Is she staying in the boathouse?' She was surprised at the easy way such a personal question slipped out and when he said, 'No,' she was surprised how relieved she was.

'Radcliffe Manor.' That was a four-star hotel and Mell said, .

'She must be very successful. Jim told me she was a

model.' Her lips curved, 'And that she makes a habit of warning the others off you.'

'Did she warn you off?'

'I think she was staking a claim.'

'Not on me.' His voice was light but the denial was flat. There had to be something, no girl that fantastic would hang around for nearly two years for nothing, it was the word 'claim' he was denying. Of course there had been an affair, probably still was, but it would be naïve to be any nosier. Anyhow, she didn't think he would tell her, and she didn't really think she wanted to know.

She finished her orange juice and he asked, 'Can I get you a refill?'

'Please, I'm supposed to keep drinking. It's in the fridge. The kitchen's the door on the left by the back door.' She watched him cross the dining room from which the stairs led up, moving among the delicate Georgian furniture and bric-à-brac without disturbing anything. But she felt as though the windows had been flung wide, curtains were blowing and ornaments were spinning and everything was on the move.

He came back carrying the glass of orange juice and asked, 'Are the portraits all your ancestors?' They looked a joyless bunch. She said,

'Every one and not a smile among them.'

'Folk didn't do much laughing, having their pictures taken, before the instant snap. Who are they?'

She looked up at the watercolour of a woman that hung on the opposite wall, with her hair piled high, a sulky mouth and prominent eyes, violet like Elizabeth's. 'Constance, born 1850. She married a rural dean and lived to be ninety. There are a few Amelias around, too.'

'I'd like to meet them.'

'Shouldn't think it would be much of a pleasure,' she said gaily, 'but I'll introduce you.'

She took him to the case of miniatures and pointed out her great-grandmother and he said, 'There's a lady who knows her worth.' There were six miniatures in the case and they all looked pompous and self-satisfied and tonight Mell could feel no affinity with any of them. She could remember none of them but all her life they had crowded in on her. And what would they think of her now, stark naked by their standards, with Barney who looked like a gypsy and might be, for all she knew? The thought made her smile and Barney asked, 'And who would he be?'

'Big isn't he?' It was the biggest oil painting in the most imposing frame. 'This is Albert, that's Amelia's father.' Glaring through his whiskers, his hand on a desk with a couple of leatherbound books, and a piece of paper with a few illegible lines.

'What does the letter say?' Barney stepped closer and she said,

'You can't tell. I've tried.'

She had when she was a child, but it was only background clutter like the books without titles. 'Could be in code,' she said. "Flee the country, all is discovered." Only he stayed to have his portrait finished and the scandal blew over.'

'Was there a scandal?'

'No. They all led very cushy, very boring lives.'

'On the surface,' said Barney. 'I think the letter reads, "Knock three times and ask for Alice".'

'If it does poor Alice must have had a shock when Albert arrived as her blind date.' The whiskers made her think of Jim and how the sun had shown up his receding chin; maybe Albert had had a weak jawline under all that hair. 'Men can hide behind a beard,' she mused. 'They don't need to face the world barefaced. I don't think that's quite fair.'

'A beard wouldn't suit you,' said Barney.

'It might right now.' And you don't need one, she thought. I could look you straight in the face and learn nothing you didn't want to tell me, and suddenly she was dizzy again. She swayed and he steadied her and she stiffened because the quick grip on her peeling arm hurt. 'I'll have to sit down.'

As soon as she was off her feet the room steadied. 'Sorry about that,' she said. 'I've been on a convalescent diet for two days. It must be too much jelly in the system; it's gone to my legs.' He was frowning, considering,

'Is there anyone else here? Shouldn't you be in bed?'

'I am all right. They had to go out. Please don't go.' She didn't want him going back to Gemma and she started babbling, 'I've done nothing but rest since Tuesday and I'm bored stiff. I'm waiting for Pammie to ring. I had to shut the shop today because Pammie gets bored on her own and I don't think she's going to offer to keep it open tomorrow, either.'

His suggestion, 'Wouldn't your mother go along?' made her laugh.

'She's no business woman. You wouldn't get her behind a counter at gunpoint.'

'Don't you have anyone you can call in an emergency?'

'I don't like asking favours.'

'Why not?'

She thought for a while. Unless she was going to close her shop she would have to ask for help, then she said, 'Anna might help. Her children are in their teens and she does sometimes do part-time work.'

'What's the number?' She told him where her personal phone book was, in a drawer in the secretaire, and he looked up the number and dialled. Then she took the phone and Anna said she would enjoy a couple of days at Rainbow's End. Barney phoned Pammie, who wasn't home, and left a message, and Mell said,

'Goodness, how simple it is,' and relaxed on the chaise longue again with that worry off her mind.

But she still didn't want to be left with only the portraits for company. 'There are too many of them for the size of the house,' she said. 'In the old place they'd be spread out more.'

'The old place?'

'We used to live somewhere else until my father died,'

she explained. 'Then it was turned into flats and we came here. My mother brought some of the furniture with us and these have got to be all the family portraits. I shouldn't think any got away.'

'I'd say you've got the set. She made a good selection with the furniture. Is the man she's chosen for you as elegant?'

'Oh, absolutely,' she drawled flippantly. 'Out of the very top drawer.'

'Then maybe you could do worse.'

'So they keep telling me. Do they tell you you could do worse than Gemma?' He grinned and she was enjoying herself. 'Only I don't want to be tied down any more than you do, and when I heard he'd got the ring I started to feel trapped. I've led a dull life, like the rest of my family.' She looked at him with dancing eyes. 'But as soon as I get my own face back I am going to widen my horizons.'

'That's always a good idea.'

They were joking but she had a purpose. 'I really don't like asking favours,' she said, 'but there is something.'

'Ask away.'

'Things happen while you're around. While you're here I think I could learn from you.'

'Anything in particular?'

'Oh,' she said, 'this and that. Will you let me tag along?'

'There's nothing I'd like better.'

'No strings of course.'

'Not a one.' And she let her head fall back on a cushion with a smile. All the time he was here she was feeling better. She even asked where Gemma was tonight and he told her, 'She went yesterday, on a modelling assignment to the Bahamas.'

'*Very* nice,' she said and he didn't seem to care. He was looking at Mell.

'What did your mother say when you arrived home in this state?'

'That it proved I'd gone ga-ga,' she said cheerfully. 'They hadn't got over the shock of me going swimming the river, that shook them rigid, so now they think I'm suffering for my sins.'

'And I thought you were starting to enjoy them,' he said with mock solemnity, and she said equally gravely,

'Oh, I intend to. I think I could go out after dark quite soon without frightening the sheep, then I can come to the dig. I'm hoping to get to the boot fair on Sunday. Will you have another stall?'

Some of the team had brought along saleable articles so they would be taking over a site on Sunday, and she offered, 'I'll get up into the attic as soon as I can; there might be something there.'

Then she heard the car turn into the drive and recognised the sound of the engine, and all the warmth went out of the room because she knew that her mother would arrive in the next few minutes. Elizabeth was home early tonight, so perhaps the gossip had centred too persistently on Robert Gunnison.

She said, 'That's my mother's car. Do you want to make a getaway?'

'Why?' he asked, which was a good question that would soon be answered. For the life of her she couldn't look relaxed. She had to lean forward, watching the open door that divided the rooms, and Barney stood up.

Elizabeth fixed her eyes on Mell and came straight for her, demanding, 'What are you doing down here and whose is the car?'

Once in the room she saw Barney and stopped dead, drawing in her breath in a little cry, and Mell could see how he must look to her mother, with his height, his breadth of shoulder, his unruly dark hair and the natural arrogance of his stance.

He was standing by a small table with a blue glass Venetian vase on it and instinctively Elizabeth cried, 'Don't touch anything.'

'*Mother!*' Mell protested, but he did have this

disturbing effect and she hid a smile. 'This is Barnaby Rudd,' she said. 'Barney, my mother, Mrs Beaumont.'

While she was speaking Elizabeth was demanding, 'What is he doing here?' as if Barney was deaf and dumb.

'He came to see why I didn't turn up at the dig this afternoon,' said Mell.

'Well if he looks at you he'll see why,' said Elizabeth, sidling round the room, her eyes fixed on him as if he was something dangerous and untamed that could go berserk any moment. Mell knew she would start to giggle soon, if it was only from nerves.

'And to see if we have any jumble they can sell at the boot fair towards the running expenses of the dig,' she said.

Elizabeth was behind a small, green velvet, button-backed chair. She stopped there, gripping the back of the chair and drawing herself up so that she looked quite tall for a petite woman, enquiring venomously, 'And whose pocket does the money go into?' The insult was deliberate and all Mell's amusement vanished.

'I could arrange for you to see the books,' Barney drawled. His voice and his face were expressionless and his stillness seemed to incense Elizabeth, leaving her quivering and twittering with outrage.

'Oh, I'm quite sure you could. I don't suppose that would be any problem at all. You must excuse me if I don't ask you to sit down but I don't remember inviting you here.'

'This is my home, too,' said Mell quietly and Elizabeth shrilled.

'But of course, you're my daughter's recent acquaintance. The man who seems to have made her lose her head and all sense of propriety.' She gave Mell a quick shuddering glance and then turned back on Barney. 'And who are you exactly? Where *do* you come from?'

'Stop it,' said Mell through gritted teeth and Elizabeth said,

'I must apologise. One doesn't ask those kind of

questions these days, does one? And if you told me I doubt if it would reassure me. But as Amelia is still unwell, I must ask you to leave immediately. That, I suppose, I am entitled to do.'

When he moved she grabbed the back of the chair even harder as though she expected him to wreak havoc before he went, and Mell made a grimace of apology. Anything she said would only make her mother more unreasonable. If she had been less washed out she would have said, 'Stop it,' a great deal louder. As it was, she bit her lip and smiled at him, which she hoped showed what she thought, and he said, 'My God, sweetheart, no wonder you need to break out.' Then he bent and kissed her mouth while Elizabeth froze.

'No!' wailed Elizabeth. *'No!'* By then Barney was out of the house so she had to be talking to Mell or herself.

'That,' said Mell, 'was a very ill-bred performance,' and Elizabeth said fiercely, 'Don't talk to me about being ill-bred when I've just found that great uncouth brute in my drawing room. I've been answering questions all night about you. I didn't stay for supper, it would have choked me, and what *has* been going on here?'

In her cotton housecoat, and bare-legged, Mell was lightly clad, but her scorched skin was hardly seductive. 'Talk,' she said. 'I'm not up to much else,' and Elizabeth's pale cheeks flamed, because that man was like a powerful animal; she would almost rather have seen Mell in the clutches of a tiger.

She said, 'He kissed you!' going stiff with distaste, and Mell thought, not really. He brushed my lips, but if he really kissed me he would touch every nerve in my body.

'And that—that ruffian,' said Elizabeth, 'is what you prefer to Robert. Now I've seen it all. I give up.' She flounced out of the room and within a couple of minutes Mell followed, going up to her own room. She could hear the taps running fast in the bathroom and knew that Elizabeth would soon be lying in perfumed water, trying to wash away the taint of the beast she had found in her drawing room.

Mell stayed where she was. She heard her mother go downstairs again, she heard Nanny come back from her meeting, and a little while later Nanny marched into Mell's room and said ominously, 'He's been here, then.'

She made it sound as if Barney had carried a sawn-off shotgun and Mell said, 'Yes, when mother came back there he was, large as life, in the lounge. He is large, I'll give you that, and although he didn't actually break anything he walked quite close to one or two things. He gave her a few anxious moments.'

Nanny held her ground, glowering for about five seconds, and then marched out again, obviously deciding she was wasting her time here. To be continued tomorrow, thought Mell, and tomorrow I must say my piece.

Next morning she dressed in loose clothing and came down to the kitchen. Elizabeth was doing without her early tea in bed while Mell was bedridden. She sat at the kitchen table with the white and gold cup before her, in a white seersucker négligé that frilled at throat and wrists, and with her dark hair loose.

Nanny had a cup of tea, too, and Mell knew they had been discussing Barney. As she walked in her mother said, 'So you're feeling well enough to come down? But of course you are, you were well enough to come down last night, weren't you?'

'Would you rather I'd entertained him in my bedroom?' asked Mell, and her mother flinched and Nanny said,

'We'd rather you hadn't entertained him anywhere, that's what we'd rather.'

Mell made herself a cup of coffee while Elizabeth went on about how nobody at the bridge party could understand why Mell hadn't snapped up Robert, as though that had been the only topic of conversation all night. It hadn't, of course, her mother was the only one who was obsessed with it, but all the same it must have been a shock for her to come home and find Barney, and now she was complaining about that. 'And I hope he doesn't imagine he is going to walk in and out of my home any time he likes.'

'My home, too,' Mell said, as she had said last night. But this morning her voice was stronger and she was the one who continued to speak. 'But if my friends can't call without being insulted, I can find another home.'

That had occurred to neither of them. Other young folk moved into digs or flats, but not Amelia. Elizabeth had looked forward to the day when Amelia would move to the Gunnison house because she could almost look on that as her own, but the idea of her daughter going out of her reach frightened her. She and Nanny would be all alone. They couldn't manage. She gasped, 'You couldn't leave home.'

'What's to stop me?' said Mell. 'But I won't, so long as you don't make it unbearable for me. Nothing terrible is happening. If you hadn't come storming in you'd have found that Barney is not an uncouth brute, which was what you called him. He's extremely intelligent. He's got a much better mind than—Robert for instance.'

'Has he?' Elizabeth muttered. She was not concerned with brain power. What she disliked and distrusted had been the animal maleness of the man. She said plaintively, 'I want you to be safe and no woman would be safe with him.'

'I won't be anything with him for long,' said Mell. 'They're only here till the end of the summer. But if I am staying in this house and I should bring any of the team home, the screeching has to stop.'

'I didn't screech,' Elizabeth protested faintly.

'You certainly did,' said Mell. 'So that nobody else could get a word in,' and Nanny tut-tutted, faced with this version of last night's scene.

'Well,' Elizabeth conceded grudgingly, 'I don't like the looks of him and I wouldn't trust him and I have always been considered a very good judge of character, but—well, perhaps I was hasty.'

She considered she had made generous amends and sipped her tea and complained because it had gone cold.

'I'll make you another cup,' Mell offered and Nanny murmured instinctively,

'There's a good girl,' as if everything was the way it used to be, although it was not and never would be again.

CHAPTER SIX

THERE was an uneasy truce that day. Mell suspected that given any encouragement her mother would have gone down with a migraine. Elizabeth spent the morning reading the newspaper and writing letters, sitting at the little secretaire in the lounge. After a phone call she announced that she would be out that evening and that if Mell was expecting company perhaps they would leave before midnight to save everyone's feelings.

'I can guarantee that,' said Mell, 'but I'm not expecting anyone.'

She was glad she had made arrangements about the shop. Although she was recovering well she was still shaky. But she could sit at the kitchen table and sketch designs, and that was where she was when the phone rang again and her mother said, 'I presume it's for you; somebody wants Mell.'

Barney said, 'I thought you'd be incommunicado.'

'What would you have done then?'

'Barged in. Seven o'clock all right? Are you up to coming as far as the boathouse?'

'Will there be a crowd?' She couldn't stand boisterous company just yet, but he said, 'Only you and me,' and she said, 'Yes please.'

When she hung up she said, 'That was——' But her mother said,

'I'd rather not know. You have to lead your own life and choose your own friends and I mustn't interfere so I would rather not know.'

Mell went back to her work and Nanny, who was washing up lunchtime soup bowls at the sink, said furiously, 'He's got that blessed hose on again, he'll get us all shot,' and tore out into the garden to do battle with Watty.

At least she can row with him, Mell thought. All my mother can do is be extra ladylike now she's being blackmailed into behaving herself. It had its funny side, especially five minutes later when Nanny staggered back into the house, arms full and trailing the blue garden hose, with Watty padding malevolently behind her.

'I'm putting this up,' Nanny announced. 'He's not to be trusted with it in the shed, it's going down the cellar.'

The hose was as hard to handle as a wriggling snake and Watty advised, 'Put it in your bedroom, missus, nobody's going to find it there,' and Nanny turned purple and Mell began to laugh.

'Down the cellar,' said Mell, 'and out of temptation. Come on, Watty, or you are going to get us into trouble. Wind it up and pray for rain.'

'I'll do it for you,' said Watty, 'and it's nothing to do with this one.' He sneered at Nanny, whipped the hose out of her hands and got it into manageable shape with quick dexterity. Mell opened the cellar door that led from the kitchen and Watty and the hose disappeared down the stone flight of steps. When he reappeared he demanded, 'Satisfied, you old crow? And don't blame me if the roses die!'

'You're making this up,' Barney said, when she told him about it.

He had arrived at her home that evening and she had been waiting. Each day she looked nearer normal and tonight, with make-up, she felt almost presentable. As the scorched skin flaked from her face she discovered freckles across her nose, and wondered if they would stay so that every time she looked in a mirror she would be reminded of this summer.

It was another sweltering night but if there had been swimmers in the river they had gone when Barney parked the car on the bank and they walked along the towpath to the boathouse. It seemed like that first evening, just the two of them, with the sheep in the meadow and the rooks cawing over the spinney, and the motor cruiser bobbing gently under the willows.

They had stopped for a Chinese takeaway, which they set out on the little table that was laid for two, with glasses for a bottle of white wine. She was hungry. Her plate was piled with spring roll and bean shoots and fried rice while Barney ate barbecued spare ribs with the trimmings, and she said she supposed the most exciting thing that had happened to her today was a fight over a garden hose.

She described Nanny and Watty and their running battle over the years and when he laughed she said, 'I am not making it up, that is how they carry on.' She built her rice into little peaks with her fork, looking down at it. 'And talking of carrying on, I'm sorry about the way my mother behaved. It's no excuse but I am upsetting her, she did have my life all mapped out.' She gave a little nervous laugh. 'She had just come from seeing her friends and none of them can understand why I'm not marrying Robert when they all thought we were so well suited; and it was rather a shock for her finding you there. Well, it is quite a small house and you are big and she thought the barbarians had come.'

'I got the impression she expected me to wreck the joint,' he said drily, and then he grinned. 'They're a nervous lot round here. Only last Sunday a total stranger nearly brained me because she thought I looked like a crook.'

'Sorry,' she gurgled. 'Prejudice must run in the family. Now of course I would trust you with almost anything. Only it breaks her heart if anything gets broken. She wants everything to stay put and she wants me to stay put, too.'

He topped up both wineglasses, asking, 'What do you want?'

She wanted to stay here, she always wanted to stay with him, although as she was still peeling and not very pretty maybe it was not such a good idea. But in a few more days she would be smooth skinned again and then

there was every chance of her getting very close indeed
to Barney. When she thought about that, excitement
surged through her so that she had to swallow before
she could say, lightly and steadily, 'Like you said last
night, I want to break out. I don't suppose you know
how it feels to be shut in.' If he had a permanent home
she was sure it was a pad where he stayed briefly and
stored a few belongings, and she joked, 'Except for a
few hours in a Greek jail.'

'And more than a few years in an orphanage.'

She might have suspected that. 'Was it grim?' she
asked quietly.

'No.' He helped himself to another dollop of fried
rice.

'You just stayed there? You weren't fostered or
anything?'

'Nobody in their right minds would have fostered me.
I was a bloody menace.'

She could see him as a dark and scowling boy, a born
rebel. As a man he lived life on his own terms and—
another of Nanny's little sayings—had found that a
smile buttered more parsnips than a frown.

'I shall wear a hat,' she said gaily, 'and break out and
have myself a lovely summer. I may make a list of the
things I've always wanted to do.'

'Like what?' She entered into the game laughing, but
if Robert had asked her instead of taking her for
granted, she might have drifted into becoming Mrs
Gunnison and never been Mell, and knowing that made
her very glad that she could still please herself.

She bit into the brittle crispness of a prawn cracker.
'Like eating Chinese food more often, drag-racing,
hang-gliding, chatting up strangers, getting drunk. I
shall be twenty-two on the twenty-eighth of this month
and I've never taken a real risk in my life, unless you
count catching sunstroke, and I didn't know I was
doing that until I fell down.'

'You've led a very deprived life,' he teased her and
she said,

'You can laugh, but how many twenty-two year old virgins do you know?'

As soon as she'd said it she wished she hadn't, and when he said, 'Not many,' she said, 'That's my story and I'm sticking to it. What have you got for the boot fair this week?'

'A mixed bag.'

'I'll find something,' she promised. 'There's bound to be something in the attic.'

He raised an eyebrow. 'But is your mother going to let it out of the attic?'

'Don't worry, I'll manage,' she assured him.

The moon was high when he took her home. The sky was glittery with stars and there was not a single cloud in sight. They had spun out the meal, eating slowly, talking, finishing the wine. It was getting late when she said, 'I really should be going,' and he said,

'I suppose you should.' He pushed back his chair from the table, and when she got up he didn't try to persuade her to stay.

'Shall I help with the washing up?' she offered and he said,

'Most of it's chuck-away.'

'Well it was nice, I'm hooked on Chinese food.'

They walked down the wooden steps and along the towpath back to the car. They chatted all the way and in the car there was music on the radio. Barney was a fantastic companion and he thought she was pretty good. It had been nice, she had enjoyed the food and the company, but he did not want her getting hooked on him. There had been no talk of sharing a bed tonight, and she did not believe it was because she was pinker than usual. It was because she had told him it would be the first time for her.

That would be a come-on to some men. She hadn't meant it to be, she hadn't meant anything, she had just *said* it. But a first-timer was an unknown quantity who might decide afterwards that she belonged.

'Can I tag along?' she had asked. 'I think I could

learn from you.' But he had presumed that a woman of her age would have had some experience. He hadn't expected to be teaching every inch of the way. Now he would wonder, if they became lovers, if it might develop into a heavy scene.

It would not. She did not want to hold on to anybody. That was one of the reasons she had backed off from Robert, and hanging on to Barney would be like trying to ride a wild horse. But she wished fervently that she had stopped to think before she admitted that she had never made complete physical love with anyone before.

When they drew up outside her home there were lights on upstairs. Downstairs was dark and as there was still half an hour to go to midnight her mother might not be home. But if she said, 'Will you come in?' he would surely say, 'You've got to be joking,' so she opened her door as soon as he stepped out of his and said, 'Good night and thanks. Shall I see you at the boot fair? I'll bring what I can collect along in the van.'

There was all tomorrow in between, but eagerness was one thing from a girl who knew her way around and quite another from one who had been a non-starter up to now. He had come round the car and he put light hands on her shoulders and kissed her lightly, as though she was a child, and her own hands almost moved to latch behind his head and pull his face down hard. But this was in the street, under a lamp post, and he had already stepped back, and as she turned she saw the shadow at the landing window.

She let herself in and Nanny stood at the top of the stairs. 'No need to ask where you've been,' said Nanny.

'No need to ask who I've been with,' said Mell, 'as you watched me go and now you've seen me come back. But where I've been is in a boathouse having a Chinese meal.'

'Nasty foreign stuff,' said Nanny. 'And your mother and Hilda Hallchurch are right, he doesn't look like a gentleman.'

'Well he behaved like one tonight, worse luck,' said Mell.

She slept badly. Even with her window wide open the room was still airless. She tossed with troubled dreams of endlessly searching for something she couldn't find, and when she opened her eyes next morning she heard herself sob. But she was steady on her feet when she got out of bed and she was first downstairs.

Nanny was grumpy and Elizabeth was cool. Mell took up her mother's tea and Elizabeth thanked her but didn't look particularly grateful. There was an opaqueness in Elizabeth's violet eyes this morning that Mell had seen before. She was distancing herself from unpleasantness. She didn't like what was happening and so, as far as possible, she would pretend it wasn't.

'I want to look in the attic,' Mell said, 'to see if there's anything we could sell at the boot fair for the dig. Is that all right?'

'I suppose so,' said Elizabeth, and Mell knew she had wanted to refuse.

She held the curtain aside from the window so that the early sun streamed in and said, 'It's another lovely day,' and Elizabeth snapped,

'I should have thought you'd have had enough of the sun, it's quite ruined your complexion.'

It hadn't done her skin much good but by the time she had soaked her face with moisturiser, made up her eyes and coloured her lips, she wasn't looking too bad. She went to the shop to collect stock for tomorrow and pay Anna and Pammie.

'Thanks for helping us out,' she said to Anna, a competent no-nonsense lady in her mid-thirties, and Anna said,

'I enjoyed it. I'm glad you're better. Heat stroke can be a nasty business but it's left you with some colour in your cheeks.'

'That's not the only thing that's putting colour in her cheeks,' said Pammie. 'Will he be at the boot fair tomorrow?' When Mell said yes, she said, 'Tell you

what, I'll bring that awful cat back. It is yours isn't it?
He did bring it for you, and I don't want it.'

Mell climbed up into the attic every Christmas to
bring down the cardboard boxes that contained the
silver tree and the decorations, and then to return them
after Twelfth Night. Apart from that, nobody came up
here and in the shadows under the eaves were articles
from the old house that had not found a place in the
new. Some wooden kitchen chairs, a heavy old screen,
its brocade panels thick with dust, some framed prints
of hunting scenes.

It was hardly Aladdin's Cave and the spotlight of her
torch landed on nothing exciting. The old sewing
machine might fetch a pound or two, and there was a
trouser press, and some bookshelves with a few dusty
books, but none of them looked worth anything. And
in a long drawer that was part of the bookshelves was a
folder containing paintings.

When she opened that the colours gleamed gemlike in
the pale light of the torch, and she carried the folder
down then went back for the heavy old sewing machine.
That was awkward to manoeuvre but she managed to
get it, and the trouser press, into the van. They were
junk, not antiques, but somebody might buy them.

Elizabeth was out and Nanny, in front of the
television in the lounge, watched Mell stagger downstairs and out of the house with her burdens. Then Mell
sat down at the phone and began to ring around. She
had never asked anybody for anything until Barney
came, but this was not for herself and it was only
jumble sale stuff she was after. She called half a dozen
numbers and explained about the excavation and they
all said that if she would come round they would try to
find her something.

'Collecting for him now are we?' said Nanny when
she got up from the phone. 'Going cap in hand to our
friends?'

'It's a good cause,' said Mell, 'and there wasn't much
in the attic.' She went upstairs to bring down the step

ladder and return it to the shed, and then to fetch the
folder. It had been protected in the drawer but there
was still a film of sticky grime on the dark blue cover
and she put it down on the dining-room table and
asked, 'Do you know anything about these?' They were
landscapes of hills and skies, scenes of streets and
buildings. All in brilliant colours and she liked them
very much.

'Oh my blessed life,' said Nanny. 'Where did you get
them?' She was at the table, looking down at the
paintings as if she expected them to burst into flames.

'In the attic,' said Mell. 'What's the matter? Who did
them?' There was a J.B. in one corner. 'John
Beaumont? My father?' Nanny nodded and Mell said,
'But that's wonderful. I didn't know he was an artist.'

'He wasn't. He was a stockbroker.'

'So this was a hobby. Well I think they're very good.'
She spread them so that they almost covered the table.
'I shall frame them.'

'No!' Nanny gasped. 'Put them back before your
mother comes home.' She began to gather them
frantically with shaking hands. 'Don't let her see them,
they'd only upset her. They'd bring back too many
memories of the old times.'

'And you think I'm causing her enough grief as it is,'
Mell said wryly. 'All right, I'll take them away.'

But she wouldn't put them back. She would take
them to the shop, to her workroom where her mother
never went, and there they would be a link for her with
the father whose face she could not remember . . .

The van was full for the boot fair, stacked with
tightly packed ware from Rainbow's End and with the
contributions for the dig fund that Mell had collected
last night. When she drove into the old airfield in the
morning she was one of the first to arrive. All around
her pitches were being claimed and stocked. The day
was hot already and the crowds would come, and there
was bustling anticipation as everyone rushed about
unloading.

Drag-racing was a once-monthly event so Pammie's father brought her this morning, and she got out of the family car clutching the china cat and said, 'He isn't up here then?'

'Who isn't?' Mell was struggling with the awning.

'Barney, I looked out for him. Most of the sites are taken but I didn't see him.' She went to the van and yelped, 'What's all this?'

'Junk for the dig pitch,' said Mell. 'When we're set up here I'll walk down and find it.'

She saw redheaded Sylvia arranging articles on a trestle table while David—the lad whom Mabel the cow had taken a fancy to—seemed to be taking a lawnmower to pieces, and they greeted her like an old friend.

'We missed you,' said Sylvia.

'Hope it hasn't put you off digging,' said David.

'I'm going off digging,' Sylvia declared. 'That's why I volunteered us for boot fair duty. It's easier on the back.'

'Just you two today is it?' Mell enquired very casually.

'Just us,' said Sylvia, which meant that Barney was not coming, so afterwards Mell would go over to the dig, and when she saw Barney she would be bright and relaxed because all she wanted from him was a relationship with no strings. She wouldn't even say, 'You weren't at the boot fair,' in case it sounded accusing.

She drove her van over the rough grass at the back to their pitch and unloaded her haul. 'See you later maybe,' she said.

The sun shone and the customers came. Mell wore her floppy hat and a dress in rainbow colours, and most of those who saw her every week thought she was looking brighter than usual. Some of it was the residue of sunburn but the vivid dress was a stunner and she was out at the front of the stall today, on the look-out for customers, instead of leaving it to Pammie and keeping in the background as she usually did.

She had been told that Barney was not coming so she was not on the look-out for him, but she saw him when he was a long way away. Like last week he came striding along, stripped to the waist, but today Mell went to meet him smiling, ready to say, 'Hallo'. That was how she was going to greet him, like a friend. But she was moving faster all the time as though her feet had wings, and at the end she ran right into his arms and didn't care who saw her. He hugged her, and they walked to her stall with his arm around her, getting curious looks from the regulars.

Pammie, fluttering her eyelashes, told him, 'She's been hopping about like a scalded cat waiting for you. I don't know what you've been doing to her but I don't think you're right for her at all. She's not used to your sort, she's used to a very different kind of feller.'

Mell choked with embarrassment, and with fury when Pammie simpered, 'But if it's a real woman you're looking for——'

'No, thank you,' said Barney, emphatically and curtly, as though he was declining a worthless offer, and the smirk was wiped off Pammie's face. She looked so shocked that Mell was almost sorry for her, although she hadn't stopped to consider Mell's feelings.

'I'm going to get a drink,' said Pammie coldly, tossing blonde curls, and she stamped off in the direction of the ice-cream van.

'She talks a lot of nonsense,' said Mell. 'I don't think she knows what she is saying half the time.'

'Like hell,' said Barney.

'Well, I hope she comes back.' Pammie was obviously deeply offended.

'I can stand in till she does.' He went to a woman who was flipping through the seconds rail. 'Can I help you, madam? Every one hand printed, all originals. This isn't your run-of-the-mill stuff, this is all designer quality.'

'Is it?' said the woman, and bought one.

Barney had a carrying voice and a powerful personality and he kept up the patter, gathering in the customers so that Mell was serving faster than ever before. On good days her sale at the boot fair was steady but this was turning into a hilarious riot.

Pammie had sat on the grass by the ice-cream van to eat her strawberry cone and drink a Coke. Then she had strolled back, not hurrying; it was too hot to hurry. She had expected to be missed and to have Mell waiting anxiously. When she heard Barney shouting, 'Rainbow's End designer wear: cheap, cheerful and colourful,' she pushed her way into the stall and round to Mell, who was folding a dress and slipping it in a bag, and demanded, 'What's he think he's doing?'

'Drumming up business,' said Mell.

Pammie darted a baleful look at Barney's back as he called across to a couple of giggling girls. 'I think he's dead common,' said Pammie primly. 'He sounds like a barrow boy.'

Oh no, thought Mell, that is a most uncommon man; and she burst out laughing. 'I'd never have believed it but you sound just like my mother.'

They went on selling, and Mell caught the infectious gaiety so that she was doing a little promoting herself. 'They're all my own designs,' she was telling them. 'All originals.' She had always thought that her clothes were good value but she had never blown her own trumpet before. Now, while Pammie was serving in more or less sullen silence, Mell laughed and joked and enjoyed herself.

The passers-by who knew her did double takes, because this was an Amelia Beaumont they hardly recognised, and who was the man who looked like a stevedore and sounded like an actor who was doing a double act with her?

Some of them asked her and she said, 'He's an archaeologist, they're excavating a Roman villa near here,' and Barney said, 'Hallo,' and they went away with something to talk about.

She had never seen Robert at the boot fair before, and she was carolling, 'All hand-printed and washable,' when their eyes met. He was frowning as if he thought his eyes were playing up, narrowing them against the sunlight and the sight of Mell shouting her wares. Not to mention the young man with the black hair and the bronzed rippling muscles who was helping her. Robert approved of none of this. She felt he might have hurried on if she had not spotted him. As it was he said, 'You're better? I heard you were under the weather.'

'It was the weather. A touch of the sun.' Her mother said it had addled her brain and Robert would agree with that and she couldn't stop smiling.

He didn't smile at all. 'Take care of yourself,' he said, and he strode off, incongruous in his sober suit among the boot fair crowds. Barney turned to her, an eyebrow quirked in query, and she said,

'Yes, that was Robert.'

'I can see why she picked him to go with the furniture.'

'I'll tell you something,' she hissed behind a hand, 'I won't be getting his mother's jewellery.'

'Was that on the cards?'

'Oh yes.'

He grinned. 'But think of all the strings that would have been attached,' and she laughed, throwing back her head. The hang-gliders were out again. It would be great to be free as a bird. She could imagine herself flying into the wide blue sky with Barney, the two of them high above the world.

Somebody touched her arm and said, 'I'll take this,' and she came down to earth again, but Barney was smiling as if he knew what she was thinking.

Not long afterwards Jock Reddie came for Barney. He drew him aside and showed him a small piece of coloured stone, held in the palm of his hand. Barney nodded and told Mell, 'I have to go. Will you come along when you're through here?'

'Yes.' It was something from the dig of course, and Barney went through the crowds so fast that Jock could hardly keep pace with him.

Beside Mell, Pammie said, 'He went pretty quick.'

The china cat was under the makeshift counter, its insane grin leering out from the shadows, and Mell bent to pat its head. 'I expect he will, but I'll always have this to remember him by.'

'I think you've gone crackers,' said Pammie, and so did her mother and Nanny when she took it home.

She went to the shop from the boot fair to replace what was left of the stock—she had made a very healthy profit today—then to the dig where she learned that the fragment of stone was a tiny square from a mosaic floor, a small portion of which had been uncovered. The team was delighted but the farmer who owned the field were less enthusiastic.

Barney and Professor Richmond had spent most of the afternoon promising William Whitehead that the excavation would not turn into a circus. Professor Richmond mentioned that this kind of find could not be explored in a hurry, and Farmer Whitehead informed them that he considered four months was ample time for anybody to be digging up his good grazing land.

But Alan, William's son, was on their side, and there was general jubilation; Mell felt as though she had stumbled into a secret land of magic and mystery. She poured over the tiny cleared section, with its geometric patterned edging, and wondered what the picture would be and if she could get a design out of any of it.

Since Tuesday, the 'finds' tent had acquired some contents and she walked through it, examining broken stone slates, a few shards of pottery, stone and concrete pieces from fallen walls, a key, a William the Fourth coin, a horseshoe and a broken clay pipe, all marked, and photographed where they were found before they were brought in here.

They were all glad to see her again. 'What did I tell you?' said Jim. 'Didn't I say that anything Barney's got a hand in is a winner?'

'I'm sure you did,' said Mell, and again she wished that she did not have to go home. She would have liked to stay with Barney, but he didn't ask her. She didn't see him alone, although when she walked towards her van he was with her.

'Will you be working tomorrow?' she asked.

'As long as the light holds. This is turning into a rescue dig. I wouldn't put it past the old devil to put the bull in the field.' He laughed, but she wondered if he meant that.

'Right,' she said, 'I'll come up and do some digging.'

'Sure you're up to it?'

'Of *course*.' She was strong and well again and she hoped he didn't think she was really delicate. She searched in her handbag for her keys and when she came up with them he kissed her. On the cheek this time, and again it was light, and again she felt the stirrings of a response that could have blotted out everything around if she had surrendered to it.

She wanted him desperately. It was as though she had been waiting for him all her life, and when he made love to her her inexperience wouldn't matter because her body would react instinctively and she wouldn't have to worry about a thing. She would simply go wild. But she had to wait until he asked. And he would, because he must.

'What is that monstrosity?' Mell's mother said when she walked into the house with the china cat.

'A present,' said Mell.

'No need to ask who from.' Elizabeth was scathing. 'It looks exactly his taste.' She really did imagine that Barney had gone into a shop and selected this, and not for laughs.

'It was a joke——' Mell began, but Elizabeth sighed.

'And when I think what Robert was going to give you for your birthday.'

'He wasn't giving me a thing,' said Mell. 'He was giving his mother's jewellery to the next Mrs Gunnison and I think the price was too high.'

She took the china cat to her room and put it on the dressing-table. It was certainly the odd one out in this house but it made her smile every time she looked at it. She closed the bedroom door when she came out because if it caught he mother's eye it could irritate Elizabeth so much that she might throw it through the window . . .

The rest of the month rushed by. Mell worked hard, in her business and at home. She was turning out some good designs. She had two of her father's pictures framed and hung them in her workroom and she felt they inspired her. When Barney saw them and she told him who had painted them he said, 'So that's where you get your feel for colour.'

'I suppose it is.'

He was studying them carefully. 'I like them,' he said. 'Why are there none of his pictures in your home? Or are there?'

'It was only a hobby,' she said. 'There are only a few sketches.' And they would not be to her mother's taste, but Mell liked them and she had known that Barney would.

He sometimes came over during the lunch hour and they ate in a local pub, or bought sandwiches and rolls from next door, and she showed him her latest styles and designs. Or she met him at the Angler's Arms, or she went to the dig and they shared their lunch there. She got up earlier and, although it was sometimes late when she came home, she was doing as much around the house as ever.

Elizabeth never let Barney's name pass her lips. When Mell tried to talk about anything connected with him Elizabeth interrupted her. 'I don't want to know. You come and go exactly as you please. Just don't tell me about it.'

Nanny hadn't forgiven Mell either. 'Off after him again tonight are we?' Nanny said most mornings, and it was always the dig because in the time remaining they could only uncover a fraction of the floor. They had reached the figure of a girl with a bird in her hand, one of the Four Seasons probably, and there was talk of getting the meadow declared a site of national interest. But the moment the farmer got wind of that he was capable of bringing in the earthshifters and ploughing it up. His family had farmed here for three hundred years and nobody was telling him what to do with his land. In the meantime work went on at all hours.

Mell saw a lot of Barney. When she was with him there was always the buzz of excitement around him but there were always other people, too. She was never again asked to stay in the boathouse but it was still the best two weeks of her life: more fun, more action, and with Barney a relationship that was never dull for a moment and was as sensual as the Kama Sutra.

Except that the activity was all in her head. In daydreams she ran her fingers through his hair and over the moving muscles of his back and shoulders. She played with the black curly hair on his chest and down the flat stomach, and touched where she hadn't seen and felt the softness grow hard and blushed warm, and the glow made her eyes shine and her lips curve so that she got compliments on how well she was looking.

At night she dreamed of him coming to her, all the things he would do to her. She started that dream while she lay in the darkness waiting to fall asleep, and with luck it carried on through the night. Sometimes she remembered a little in the morning and came downstairs looking smug.

That didn't improve Nanny's or her mother's temper and she could hardly explain to them, 'I've never fantasised about a man before. I'm very good at it and it has to be some sort of practice for when the real thing happens to me. Which should be any night now . . .'

CHAPTER SEVEN

NANNY had baked the birthday cake and decorated it and now it stood on the dresser, but there was to be no party. Mell's birthday was the day she should have been getting engaged to Robert and for Nanny and Elizabeth that morning there was nothing to celebrate.

Nanny gave Mell a box of vellum stationery, and her mother produced a small bottle of Diorissimo, which was Elizabeth's favourite perfume that her friends brought her duty-free from holidays abroad.

Elizabeth had come down, instead of waiting to have her tea carried up, to see what was in the mail. She was looking for something from Robert. Mell opened cards and read out names and when she said, 'Robert,' Elizabeth asked eagerly,

'What does he say?'

'Robert,' said Mell. The front was embossed in a bouquet of flowers with 'Best wishes' printed inside and Robert's signature.

'Well at least he thought of you, I suppose that's something,' said her mother. 'You could get in touch with him. Or I could phone him myself and invite him round tonight.'

'No!' Mell said wildly. 'I'll be late. I'm going out. I don't know when I'll be back. Don't anyone wait up.'

She fled, and she was getting into her van when Watty came up with a great grin and a red rose. He dived into his jacket pocket. 'I got you some humbugs. You have a good birthday now.'

'Oh, thank you.' She took the bag of sweets and the rose. 'I'm going to have a smashing birthday.'

He was pleased to hear it. 'Time you started going your own way. Between you and me and the gatepost I always thought that Gunnison was a dried up old stick.

Coming from Watty, who looked as though he hadn't a drop of juice in him, that was rich, but Watty certainly had a more youthful spirit than Robert. 'Pity your father left it too late,' he said as the engine caught and revved, so that she was not quite sure what she heard. But her father had died young, he must have missed out on many things.

Barney was taking her out tonight. It was a Saturday. Weekends were coming and going time on the dig. Some left, some arrived; any time off the regulars had to have was usually taken then. Yesterday Barney had asked her, 'What will you be doing tomorrow night?' and she had said,

'Nothing,' because she knew that her birthday at home would be a time of reproaches.

'We'll get a meal out shall we?' he'd suggested. So when she shut the shop she would go to the dig, and then they would have an evening more or less alone and it would be a smashing birthday.

Pammie bought her a chocolate gateau and ate most of it, and Mell gave herself a birthday present of a silk dress out of stock. There was no pattern on this and the style was simple, sleeveless, cut in a low V at the neck and a deeper one at the back, but the skirt flowed beautifully and the colour was the bright yellow of laburnums.

Just after six, Mell had redone her make-up, changed from working clothes into the yellow dress, and was on her way to the dig. She sang as she drove along; she would not have changed places with anyone in the world. This was her birthday treat and she was going to enjoy every minute, wherever they went, whatever they did.

The van could probably have found its own way by now, she took the road to Ruddington so often. Even if Barney had not been there she would still have found the excavations enthralling, but she wouldn't have come every day and not with this mounting excitement the nearer she came. She always arrived with her heart going like a steam-hammer because if he wasn't waiting for her she knew where to find him, because he was always here.

He was waiting now, crossing the courtyard towards her as she parked. When she got out of the van he said, 'You're looking good.'

'It's the silk. There's something flattering about silk.' She swished the skirt. 'You're looking very tidy yourself,' she said.

Tidier than she had ever seen him. He had always been in jeans. Now he wore beige slacks and a light beige polo-necked sweater and for a moment it surprised her as something out of character, although there was no reason on earth why it should. In fact, he looked terrific.

'Where are we going?' she asked. 'I know a few places we might get in.' A midsummer Saturday night often needed booking ahead.

'So do I.' He took her arm, walking her towards the towpath.

'The boathouse?'

'No.'

'Are we walking?' There were riverside pubs and hotels but the nearest was miles away.

'No.'

'Not swimming?'

'Could be.' She laughed and left it, and he made her laugh again, taking off Professor Richmond and Farmer Whitehead arguing about more time for the dig, managing to look and sound like a thin man and a fat man, Professor Richmond very erudite and earnest, William Whitehead doing a lot of grunting.

They reached the boathouse and the little cabin cruiser at its mooring under the willows. He jumped aboard and held up his hands to her. 'Come on?'

'Is it all right?'

'It's Alan's. Tonight it's ours.' The deck shifted slightly as she dropped down and his hold tightened, and as always the contact sent her whole nervous

system singing. When he held her she never wanted him
to let go but he always did. He freed the mooring and
steered the little craft into deeper water and asked, 'Do
you know anything about boats?'

'No, but I like this one.' She sat at the rail and he sat
with a hand on the wheel, and although there was not
enough breeze to stir a leaf in the trees coolness rose
from the water.

The river was drought low, leaving a narrow strip of
shingle beach where it usually lapped high up the
banks, but it was a busy stretch of water on this
summer evening. They passed other craft, from row-
boats to a pleasure steamer. A flotilla of canoeists went
by in bright red club colours, and fishermen still
huddled over their rods. She watched the ducks and the
swans and the walkers on the towpath, and at one of
the houses whose gardens ran down to the river there
was a marquee pitched on a lawn. Guests in wedding
finery were out and music was playing over loud-
speakers. Two small bridesmaids, their skirts hunched
high, were paddling from the shingle. It was not a house
Mell knew but she wished them well, and she heard
herself sigh and Barney asked, 'What's that for?'

They had done very little talking. It was peaceful and
pleasant, but the wedding scene had brought back some
of this morning's tension because it was exactly what
her mother had wanted for her. She said, 'Things were
strained at home this morning. Today was the day I
was expected to get engaged to Robert and this
morning I was nobody's favourite.'

'Happy birthday,' he said.

'How did you——?' Then she remembered telling
him she would be twenty-two on the twenty-eighth. 'It
got better,' she said. 'Watty gave me a bag of humbugs
and a red rose, and Pammie gave me a chocolate cake.
We cut some of it up for the customers and it went
down a treat. And now I'm on a cruise.'

'Look in the locker under the berth on the left,' he
said.

She had already stepped down into the cabin, with its two long seats that would open into berths, its folding table and tiny galley and minute toilet cabin. It had seemed claustrophobically small and she had come up again quickly for air. But now she went back and found the locker. There was a biscuit tin inside that didn't look particularly new. She carried it up and asked, 'Shall I open it?'

'Yes.'

Everything glittered. It was full of costume jewellery: chains, bracelets, earrings, rings, pins, all sparkling bright. As a collection it must have cost him enough to have bought one fairly good piece and her mother would have called it a waste of money, but it was all wearable and she would have fun wearing it. She dipped in and brought up a trailing chain. 'All for me?'

'Well, you missed out on Robert's.' He's cheering me up she thought. It's to make me smile, like the china cat.

She picked out a ring that had a huge 'diamond'. Robert's mother's engagement ring was a cluster of genuine gems and it was the right size for Mell's finger. She shivered at the thought and her fingers closed over the paste ring. She almost slipped that on her left hand but she stopped in time and put it on the right. It was large enough to twist round but it flashed colours in the light of the setting sun and she said, 'I feel like someone who found the treasure at Rainbow's End.'

She sounded like a child ... And they all lived happily ever after ... But there would be no ever after with Barney, and she shrugged away the shuddering feeling that sometime, someday, Mrs Gunnison's ring might still be waiting.

She held up a waterfall earring, a cascade of tiny white stones, and took out her little gold stud and slipped that in instead. Then the other one, moving her head so that they swung against her cheeks, and looking towards Barney for approval. 'Fantastic,' he said.

'Where's my bag? I want a mirror.' But he was steering towards a landing stage and there was no time to try on any more.

The Lobster Pot was a seafood restaurant in what had once been a small boatyard. There were moorings, although most of the diners came by car. Inside, the ceiling was draped with fishing nets and hung with coloured floats and ships' lanterns. Outside, facing the river, the boatyard had been turned into a reasonable copy of a fishing village, with coils of rope and lobster pots and a small upturned dinghy. The tables were spaced around on the cobblestones and the food was good.

Mell had never been here but she had heard it was worth a visit and she was pleased to find herself stepping ashore at the Lobster Pot for her birthday treat. It was almost full but Barney had booked a table where they sat with enormous seafood platters, garlic bread and a bottle of champagne, and she was having her best birthday ever. Some of it was the champagne, some of it was because she felt pretty and bright as the swinging earrings. And most of it was Barney.

She did her share of the talking. This place was like a little bit of Cornwall and she liked Cornwall and they talked about that. Her mother had friends with holiday homes and some who had retired to sunny exotic places. All Elizabeth's friends were quite well off, she was uncomfortable with anyone who was struggling to make ends meet. And Elizabeth Beaumont was beautiful and a charmer and invited around. Sometimes Amelia went, too, because Amelia was a nice girl who got in nobody's way and always made herself useful.

So she had stayed in villas in Spain, a flat in Amsterdam, luxury apartments on Capri and Malta. Barney knew everywhere. They swapped memories but he had travelled rough and a lot further, and without doubt had learned a lot more.

She had schoolgirl French and a smattering of Italian. When she asked 'Do you speak Italian?' he said 'Yes.'

'Any others?'

'Enough to get by in most places.'

Enough to say goodbye, she thought, because you don't stay long anywhere. And she asked, 'Do you have a home?'

She hadn't asked him that before and when he said, 'The top floor of a house in Bath,' she blurted,

'Where does Gemma live?'

'Bath.'

'In the same——' She put out an outstretched hand as though that would hold back the words. 'No. Sorry. Don't answer, it's none of my business.' He would probably say yes and she didn't want to hear that. She drank the last of her champagne and the bubbles made her wrinkle her nose and he said,

'You didn't have freckles before.'

'You're the only one who's noticed that. I must have had freckles once because I can remember somebody saying, "The sun's kissed you".' Nanny maybe, although it might have been her father. Since she found those paintings he had been on her mind. It was years since she had thought about him at all but these days he did seem to be cropping up. 'Although the sun didn't settle for kissing me, I was *ravished*.'

They had sat over their meal through a spectacular sunset, through dusk, and now it was night. But it was still bright as day out here, with light streaming through the restaurant windows and little lamps on all the tables. She had drunk more than her share of champagne and had a Grand Marnier liqueur still to go. Barney was eating cheese. It had been a very good meal. Mell had chosen profiteroles and the tip of her tongue flickered between her lips, licking away a smear of chocolate and making her drawled, 'I was *ravished*,' sound very lascivious. She was fooling and he was smiling.

'Mind you,' she said, 'there are times when a little ravishing wouldn't come amiss.'

'That could be useful information.'

'Top secret, but let me finish this,' she tapped the rim of her liqueur glass, 'and I might be persuaded to tell all.'

Their coffee cups were empty. 'I'll get some more,' he said. He took the cups into the restaurant and she speared her last profiterole. He could be sobering her up with black coffee although she was sober enough, just happy because she had had a lovely evening. He was the one who had to take the boat back to Ruddington and he was sober as a judge. So was she when she realised that the evening was ending.

Oh, how she wished that this place was what it pretended to be, a fishing village with the sea lapping the landing stage, not an inland river, and the little boat called *Misty* a craft that was capable of sailing across the world.

She wished they had come ashore for a meal, and now they were going back to a floating home, to lie in each other's arms tonight, and see dawn break over some bay, where Barney could make himself understood because he spoke the language and she could walk barefoot to market to buy bread and fruit and whatever was for sale that looked tasty and wholesome.

'It is Amelia, isn't it?' said Alec Wilton. He had last seen her at the drag-racing, a little dishevelled because she had just missed being mown down by that car whose tyre burst but still looking prim, and he had heard that her affair with the middle-aged solicitor was washed up.

But although he recognised her he still asked, because it was like one of those before-and-after pictures in his sister's magazines. She was glowing, really something, and when she smiled he found himself gulping, 'I'm here with some friends. Not bad is it? I suppose you're not on your own.'

He could see by the table that she wasn't but he wished she was, and this was more of a compliment than getting value for money when she had the van serviced where he worked. Or than having him sit on the grass beside her at the drag-racing. Tonight he was dazzled, almost stammering, and it gave her confidence another boost. She had gained in confidence recently. It came from the wolf whistles and the way she was looked at differently. At the dig Jim was held back by the fact that she only had eyes for Barney, and he warned her continually that when Barney moved on he never looked back, and she always smiled and said, 'I know.'

When Barney arrived with the coffee now Alec gulped again. He had been asking what she was doing these days and if she ever had a free evening, when this man stepped up. Alec remembered him from the drag-racing and a nod of recognition passed between them, and at the same time Mell saw Alec give way. There was something in Barney's eyes, in the smiling set of his mouth, that would have made her very careful if she had been his antagonist. The two men exchanged a few amiable words and Alec went back to his friends.

She finished her liqueur and sipped her coffee, delighted that Barney was not having Alec chatting her up. That was stressing that this was their night, when they didn't want anyone but themselves. That was what Barney had said about the *Misty*. 'It's Alan's, but tonight it's ours,' and she wouldn't think beyond tonight.

'I should phone home,' she said. 'It's later than I expected. Is there a phone?'

'Straight through the dining room, past the bar. But surely it isn't that late?'

It was coming up to eleven o'clock and she was twenty-two today and it wasn't late. 'And I need the Ladies,' she said.

She took her purse. The dining room was still full but she caught the attention of a barman at the end of the bar and asked for a large vodka and tonic which she carried into the cloakroom. Two women were repairing make-up and chatting in voluble French and Mell gulped down her drink, wincing as it burned her throat, put the glass carefully aside and took a look at her own reflection. She had dazzled Alec, who had never asked for a date before and she had known him most of her life. She had never been more desirable than she was tonight, and this last drink was going to give her the courage to make the best of it.

She did phone home. She stood in a little alcove, with music playing around her, and told her mother, 'I'm at a party.'

'Whose party?' her mother demanded.

'Mine I suppose,' said Mell. 'It is my birthday. I won't be back tonight, I shall go straight up to the boot fair in the morning.' Her mother was asking where she was when she hung up.

Barney was settling the bill as she came back into the boatyard and she looked across at him weak-kneed, because he was so right for her. A man whose casual touch stirred her like a caress, whose caresses would surely blow her to pieces. She could hardly go home now. She had burned her boats as the saying went, although *Misty* was still bobbing on the water.

She almost giggled but she had bought that last drink to give her courage not send her silly, and she took a deep steadying breath before she went across to the table and he stood up. 'Shall we go?' he said.

When the lights and the music from the Lobster Pot were left behind silence settled on the river. Even the moored boats along the banks seemed empty, with only an occasional light burning. Mostly they were grey shapes, hushed and still. The towpaths were deserted, and when they took a bend in the river and reached fields and rising hills bathed in moonlight the only sounds were the hoot of an owl and the throb of the *Misty*'s engine.

And her own heartbeats. They seemed so loud that she wondered if he could hear them too, beating so hard that her chest hurt. They had hardly spoken since they reached quiet waters. Perhaps he had forgotten she was here. He wasn't looking at her, he was looking ahead, and she was very still sitting by the rail, but she had to speak before she sobered up completely. Right now there was an unreality about it all, something dreamlike, and she knew her way around in dreams.

'Don't let's go back yet,' she babbled. They were coming to a clump of trees and she pointed towards them. 'Let's moor over there.'

'Would that be a good idea?'

'Oh yes, it would.' She had never been more sure of anything but she held her breath until he turned the little boat towards the bank. She daren't move until the engine died and silence enveloped them, then she stood up and went to him.

He took her face in his hands and looked down at her, and her breath caught again. 'Your friend wasn't talking nonsense,' he said. 'I'm not the kind of man you're used to. I'm not right for you.'

What friend? Oh, *Pammie*! 'How could she know?'

'There's a lot about me you don't know,' he said quietly and she smiled because that was true but there was a lot she did know. 'I know you're here.' she said. 'That's what matters. And that nobody knows where we are and no one is expecting me home till morning and I want you to make love to me.' Her arms slid around his neck. 'Don't you want that?'

'Of course I do,' he said, and she could feel the warmth and hardness of his body like a fever in her own skin. She stumbled down the three steps to the little cabin and it was darker down there, all shadows except for the hatchway and the round windows of the portholes. The boat was rocking slightly but she reached one of the bunks.

Oh God! She was wild about him. She was hollow and aching, starving for him, burning up and silently crying, Please come, please take me, please have me and hold me. She slipped her thin silk dress from her shoulders, down to her waist. She had gone braless, her breasts were firm and smallish, and she held out her arms to him.

The breadth of his shoulders blotted out the moonlight, and she reached for him and he took one hand and sat down on the bunk beside her. Her hair was falling over her face and he tucked a strand behind her ear and said, 'Sure it isn't the champagne?' and she could see he was smiling and could hear the smile in his voice.

It shattered the dream. He had said he wanted to make love to her but he was in no hurry. He was going to go on about not being right for her and the last thing she wanted was talk. She wanted touch: lips, tongue, hands, all of him, with no time to think; soaring in mindless delight like the dreams and the fantasies, and frustration almost had her screaming.

'You need to think about it?' She wasn't screaming but she had to keep her teeth clenched to hold her voice in. 'You said you wanted to make love to me so what's to think about? You won't get saddled with me. I'm not Gemma.'

'No, you're not Gemma,' he agreed, and she began to tug her dress up again over her shoulders, so impatiently that she heard the fragile silk tear.

'Easy.' He put out a hand and she was awkwardly perched. Somehow she had squirmed up until she was sitting with her feet tucked at the side. She went to push him away, and missed and overbalanced and slid down between the bunks in a sprawling heap.

He laughed and picked her up and all the repressed tantrums of her childhood surfaced. She hammered her fists against him and once she had started she couldn't stop. She wanted to beat some sense into him because this was so *stupid*, such a wasted opportunity they might not get again. When he tried to hold her off, still laughing, she kicked out, and if he had let her go she would have come at him again.

She was carrying on like a spoiled brat and in the end he had her pinned down on the bunk and she was gasping, 'What's stopping you? What's wrong with me?'

'Nothing's wrong with you,' he said. 'You're

irresistible.' He kissed her lightly and the anger left her and she lay there wondering what was happening. 'Irresistible but smashed,' he said.

'I am not smashed.' Hardly at all, not at all now. She had lost her head because she hadn't been able to handle this. She had no experience and it had mattered so much. That was her mistake, letting it matter so much, because if he thought she was becoming serious it would be the end. And she was not. She knew it wouldn't last, that there were to be no pleas and no promises.

'I've had a lovely evening,' she said, 'but as it's my birthday I thought the least you could do was make love to me.' He was right over her, holding her wrists down on the cushion behind her head, and he had just kissed her. 'We might as well,' she said. 'We've started so we might as well finish.' She smiled and he loosed her and she put her arms round his neck again and they were both laughing.

'A girl could fall off this bunk,' she said. 'Do they push together?'

'That's the way of it.' She wondered if Gemma had been here. It was likely, and probably others. She would remember tonight but he might not because she could give him nothing he had not had before. She remembered Gemma's sensuous body and the sexual know-how she exuded, and thought crazily, Maybe he'll remember me as the one who fought, I'll bet that's never happened to him before. And the one he gave a biscuit tin full of treasure.

She had put the tin on the other bunk before they moored the *Misty* and went ashore, and now she asked, 'We are staying, aren't we?'

'Why not?'

So she had the night and she would play it lightly and not get intense, because that was the kind of relationship they had. She said, 'Do lights go on down here?'

He switched on the two wall strips that shed a mellow

light and when the two bunks were pushed together
they almost filled the cabin. She sat, cross-legged, her
pile of jewellery before her, and Barney lay at the other
end, long, long legs crossed at the ankles, arms linked
behind his head. She tried everything on, holding her
small handbag mirror to see how she looked, and he
invented stories so that it all sounded fabulous.

The gold chains were from Vilcabamba, the lost city
of the Incas, the silver linked collar from the tomb of a
Pharoah's daughter. This ring had been Elizabeth
Taylor's, that snake bracelet had belonged to Lucrezia
Borgia—scratch yourself on that and you'd had it!

She loaded herself until—except for the earrings—she
was wearing the lot. 'It certainly beats Mrs Gunnison's,'
she said. 'It must have taken you years to get all this
together. It must be the collection of a lifetime.'

'Actually it was a job lot off Stratford market with a
reduction for quantity.'

'But doesn't it suit me? I may not be the sexiest girl
you ever saw but you won't meet many who glitter so
well.' When she stretched out her arms the paste stones
and the bright metals gleamed and sparkled.

'You light up the cabin,' he said.

She began to take them off again, replacing them in
the biscuit tin, fiddling with the fastening of a chain.
'Would you——?'

When he touched the back of her neck she controlled
the shiver that ran down her spine and the urge to cling
to him. But she smiled up slantingly and when his
fingers stayed, although the necklace slithered off, she
turned her head so that they brushed against her cheek
and then her lips.

He sat down beside her and she lay back so that they
were lying together, facing each other. Go easy, she
warned herself, don't get carried away. This is warm
and caring and we are friends, but don't go overboard
even if you have burned your boats.

But it was lovely. She had never been caressed like
this. He kissed her shoulders and stroked her back,

kissing and stroking, and she felt safer than she had
ever felt in her life. She had never kissed or been kissed
like this. Her lips parted and his kiss went deeper. She
had not known that the mouth was such an instrument
of pleasure, that tongues were not just for tasting but
for playing and exploring. And ears. He was eating her
ears, in tiny delicious nibbles, penetrating them with his
tongue; and then just above the right shoulder blade he
was biting and licking and she decided that was the thing
she liked best in the world. That was her erogenous
zone, her right shoulder blade. Until his fingertips took
a line of fire down her spine to her waistline, round the
hipbones, curving under her buttocks, and all the way
she was unfolding, opening, becoming alive as electric
currents galvanised her.

She was not surrendering, she was answering every
move, and it was nothing like dreams. It was savage, and
if this was how the barbarians took their pleasure, the
water nymphs would probably have devoured them,
because they would have given no quarter either. What
he wanted from her was what she needed from him and
as he engulfed her she arched herself up to meet him
and the world exploded around her . . .

When she woke the world was moving very slightly.
The world was the boat and she had a memory of being
rocked as gently in gentle arms before she fell asleep.
Bright blue sky showed through the portholes and there
was a smell of coffee and bacon frying. She lay quite
still, facing away from the cabin. Her eyes were heavy-
lidded and she felt deliciously drowsy.

I wasn't a twenty-two year old virgin for long, she
thought, and she stifled a giggle. There should have
been pain, was there? If there was there had been no
fear and by then she probably couldn't tell the
difference between pleasure and pain, it was all a white
hot ecstasy. It beats dreams, she thought. It beats
anything I could possibly have imagined.

'Coffee?' he said.

She hadn't thought he knew she was awake. She

murmured, 'Mmm.' It was an effort to turn and look at
him, although she was very much awake now. She was
wearing nothing. She did have a sheet over her and she
clutched that convulsively although it was a bit late for
covering up. Mornings-after were another new experience that could be terribly embarrassing. Everything
could have changed.

He was only wearing slacks but she had seen him like
that dozens of times. He handed her a cup of black
coffee and asked, 'How do you like your bacon?'

'I—I'm not much for breakfast.'

'An apple?' He took one out of a tiny cupboard in
the galley and lobbed it to her. It landed beside her on
the bunk, red and shiny as Snow White's poisoned
apple. But it was firm and sweet when she bit into it
and there was something in biting into a big apple that
took the tension out of you. By the time she reached the
core, and had drunk some of the coffee, she was less
embarrassed and almost at ease.

He was swigging coffee and flipping over the bacon,
and he would be relaxed because a girl in his bed would
be nothing new to him but she wouldn't think about
that. 'What time is it?' she asked.

He checked his watch that was lying on the draining
board. 'Ten past eight.' She finished her coffee.

'I'd better get along to the shop and stock up for the
boot fair.' Her dress and her pants were at the bottom
of the bunk and she pulled on the pants and held up the
dress. The tear was tiny but she would find something
else to wear. 'If I want a good pitch I'd better hurry,'
she said.

'Do you have to turn up?'

'It's a weekly arrangement, there's nothing booked
ahead.' Mell rarely missed but Pammie did when she
got a better offer and this Sunday it was a day at the
sea. 'Pammie isn't going,' said Mell, 'I don't have to.'

They got out a map and she closed her eyes and
stabbed down a finger that landed on Cheddar Gorge.
First they went to the shop where she changed into a

white cheesecloth dress. Watty's red rose was in a
single-stem vase on the desk by the telephone and she
said, 'When Watty gave me the rose and the humbugs
he said it was time I started going my own way.'

'I like the sound of Watty,' said Barney, and Mell
laughed. 'He's the only one in our house who might
approve of you.'

Hordes of holidaymakers were swarming along the
wooded footpaths between the green and grey peaks of
the Gorge, but she was so conscious of the physical
aliveness of her own body and Barney's that the rest
could have been marching ghosts. When she remembered today she would think of them being alone.
Even standing in queues, and brushing shoulders in
crowds, Barney's touch, his voice and his smile, seemed
her only human contact.

She would recall how clear the lake was, mirroring
the scenery, and then every detail of the fantastic
fairyland of the caves in all their incredible colours, but
she would have forgotten the people.

It was cold in the caves, with four hundred feet of
solid rock overhead, like a foretaste of winter, but so
long as she held Barney's hand she glowed with
happiness . . .

All through August the long hot summer went on. The
earth was crying out for rain. Watty carried the
washing-up water and the bath water down to the roses.
So did Mell, and so did Nanny after dark when she
knew that Watty wouldn't see her.

At the dig the 'finds' tent was beginning to look like a
mini-museum with pieces from glass vessels, parts of
pots in red Samian ware, and one crushed silver
bracelet, all turned up in recent weeks. The mosaic floor
was being slowly uncovered and William Whitehead's
resistance was being slowly eroded. He was promising
nothing but the chances of this becoming a permanent
site were improving. Mell had still not asked Barney
how this might affect his plans, if he might stay on. She

was scared he would say no, so she took each day as it came.

And each day was fantastic. When he was around she was really alive, really happy, but at the end of August he was away for a week. On business he said, staying in his flat in the house in Bath where Gemma might be living, but he said nothing about Gemma and neither did Mell.

She said lightly, 'See you Saturday,' when she left him on Monday. They had been for a meal with a group from the dig and he dropped her outside her home and she scrambled hastily out of the car. She hated the thought of him not being here but she mustn't say, 'Don't go,' or, 'I shall miss you.'

She missed him. She was busy, but she counted the hours until he would be back, and she couldn't tell anybody. Pammie would soon have said she was getting too dependent, and there would be no sympathy at home. Last week Elizabeth had been at a dinner party that included Professor Richmond and come back to say, in great surprise, 'He seems to think very highly of that young man.' But Barney had never been inside the house again after that first appalling evening, although Mell had taken him down the garden to introduce him to Watty.

He had had Watty cackling with laughter and been invited into the potting shed to meet Watty's mates, a male preserve where Mell rarely intruded. 'I like him,' Watty had told her later, 'But he doesn't strike me as the settling-down kind.'

'Far from it,' Mell had said. 'Has Nanny told you he's a gypsy?'

She half expected Barney to phone her while he was away but he didn't, and that could have meant that Gemma was with him, a corrosive thought she dare not linger on. What Barney did when he was not with her did not concern her, but she had to keep reminding herself of that.

On Thursday, after work, she walked into the house

slap-bang into Robert. It was a shock. She hadn't
noticed his car, which must have been parked up the
road, but there he was, sitting in the chair he used to sit
in in the lounge, just like old times.

She had had a busy day, carving blocks for a new
design series. She hadn't stopped to comb her hair or
touch up her make-up before coming home for a bath,
so that her hair was tumbling on her shoulders, her face
was shiny and her hands were grubby. But Robert
seemed pleased to see her. His 'Hallo' was quite jovial.

Her mother, of course, looked as if she had spent the
afternoon in the beauty parlour, and her pained
expression made Mell smile and say, 'Sorry, but I have
just come home from work. I need a wash. Nice to see
you, Robert, how are you?'

He said he was keeping fit and she was looking well,
and she was glad he was not offended. As a family
friend there was a place for Robert Gunnison in the
Beaumont household. Her mother and he had a lot in
common, and Nanny enjoyed cooking for him. There
was a place laid for him tonight. Mell noticed that when
she glanced down at the dining-table on her way
upstairs, and when she came down again Nanny was
bringing in covered dishes from the kitchen.

This week Mell had been home in the evenings. So
this week she had sat at the table for the evening meal,
and her mother had chattered about all manner of
trivial things the way she always did. Nanny had talked
prices—what the drought was doing to the vegetables—
and Mell had let her thoughts drift.

Tonight was livelier because Elizabeth was delighted
to have Robert there. She flattered and flirted, and it
was like all those other evenings except that Mell was
no longer on offer. He enjoyed his meal. 'I really
shouldn't,' he said, passing his plate for a second
helping of bakewell tart and cream, and Elizabeth
laughed like the tinkle of silver bells.

'You don't need to watch your weight. You're a fine
figure of a man.'

Oh yes, you do, thought Mel, you're pear-shaped: a narrow chest, a little pot tum and a big bottom. And she remembered Barney's mahogany brown shoulders, and how they narrowed to lean hips and flat stomach, with a desperate longing, and hoped with all her heart that he was not with Gemma.

The food in her mouth suddenly tasted of ashes and when the phone rang she jumped up. She had grabbed the receiver before anyone else could move, but it was a girl she had gone to school with, who lived at Eastbourne and still kept in touch. The last time Lisa rang Mell's future had looked like being Robert, and Lisa asked about him and Mell had to say, 'Fine, yes, how are you?'

Lisa's husband wanted to get into politics, and she thought her own life was vastly more interesting than Mell's. She told Mell her news and then said, 'Anything been happening to you?'

'Not a lot,' said Mell. Nothing she was telling while her mother and Robert was listening.

'Bye then,' said Lisa, 'and don't forget to ask me to the wedding.'

Mell returned to the table and made herself smile and told them what Lisa had told her, that Geoffrey had been adopted as a Parliamentary candidate for the next election. She entered into the discussion that followed, anxious that her mother should not suspect how disappointed she was that the call was not from Barney. Nor that she was discovering twenty-four hours a day how terribly she missed him.

It was like believing you were a powerful swimmer, then having a lifebelt snatched away and finding yourself floundering and sinking. She could keep afloat without him but it was going to be a desperate struggle.

Robert stayed for coffee and when he said good night he held Elizabeth's hand and she said sweetly, 'You're always welcome here, you know that.' Then he took Mell's hand and squeezed and patted it and said,

'This has been a very pleasant evening.'

'Yes indeed,' said Mell.

Elizabeth went to the door with him while Mell carried the coffee pot into the kitchen where Nanny was dozing over a book. She was putting the cups on a tray in the lounge when Elizabeth came back, and before her mother could speak she said, 'No.'

'He still——' her mother began and Mell repeated, 'No!' so fiercely that Elizabeth gasped and didn't argue, and Mell woke Nanny and sent her to bed. Elizabeth had already gone upstairs. Then Mell finished the washing up and the putting away, and set the kitchen table for breakfast and her mother's early morning tea tray. She did it all quickly and automatically, but once in her bedroom she found she was shaking.

It was the squeeze and the pat that had done it. Her flesh crawled at the thought of Robert caressing her. Never in a million years could he replace Barney, and it was not only Robert. When Barney went she might as well take a vow of chastity because she would never want anyone else. She knew with utter certainty that this kind of sexual chemistry only came once in a lifetime. The thought of seeing him again on Saturday made her weak with longing, although she must never cling to him. She had no claim and no hold, but what she did have was enough to send her smiling to bed.

She was later than usual getting home next day. She had been at the wholesalers all afternoon choosing materials for her autumn lines, but Watty was still in the garden, spraying the blackfly off the honeysuckle. As she got out of the car he said, 'Barney came.'

She hadn't expected Barney till tomorrow and she looked around for him. 'Your mother called him in,' said Watty. 'Said she wanted to talk to him.'

'Oh no.'

'I reckon he went after that,' said Watty.

'They don't learn, do they?' said Mell, and she went fuming into the house.

The kitchen door was closed, Nanny was probably in there. But her mother was playing the piano in the lounge with that door open, and Mell went towards her. Elizabeth watched her daughter's approach with huge apprehensive eyes and Mell asked wearily, 'What did you say to him this time?

'The music flowed on so that it seemed like the background to a TV scene and nothing to do with Elizabeth, who was looking at Mell, not the keyboard. She said plaintively, 'I want you to be happy. I wanted Robert for you but——' She sighed and shrugged and her fingers went on playing.

'It's a very big but,' said Mell wryly.

'And then,' said Elizabeth, 'I thought, well it could be worse.' Mell's eyebrows rose. 'He does own a Regency house in Bath and he does have a string of degrees and he does earn a very fair living.'

Barney? Did he? Her mother seemed to have made it her business to find out that Barney was financially acceptable, but his solvency was none of Mell's concern and she said, 'So what?' as Elizabeth said, 'I suppose you imagine you're in love with him?'

She was not that foolish, but somehow she couldn't say, 'I don't imagine anything of the kind.' She said instead, 'Stop playing that damned piano,' and Elizabeth took her hands from the keys and looked down at them as if she didn't quite know where to put them.

She settled for clasping them, and her lips were as tight as her white-knuckled fingers. 'You and he have— been together, spent nights—together.' Each time her voice caught as if she could hardly get 'together' out, and yet it was the most wonderful word in the world.

'Well I told him,' she said, '"This may be a game to you but it's no game to Amelia. She has been sitting here night after night, just waiting for a call from you. My daughter," I said "would never give herself to a man unless she was very, very serious about him. So how about you?" I said. "Are you serious about her? When are you going to marry her?".'

CHAPTER EIGHT

'WHAT did he say to that?' Mell's voice, when she spoke, was so strangled that she hardly recognised it and her mother said,

'He laughed.' Elizabeth twisted her fingers together. 'Well, he smiled as if he thought I was a fool.' She sounded like someone repeating a difficult message, taking it slowly and getting every word right. 'He's very fond of you. You enjoy each other's company, he said, but it was not serious. You know that, he said.' She was at the end of her message and her brow was creased as though she couldn't work it out. 'Do you know that?'

'Of course I do,' said Mell.

'But if you know he isn't a marrying man why do you chase after him all the time?' This was beyond Elizabeth's comprehension. 'Making yourself cheap,' she added and Mell quipped,

'Cheap and cheerful, that's me.' Her mother winced and went on,

'You let him—make love to you.' Now it was Elizabeth sounding strangled as if that had been the ultimate sacrifice. 'And what are you getting in return?' she wailed. 'No security, no guarantees.'

'Believe me, I'm getting a great deal,' said Mell and Elizabeth's pale cheeks flamed.

'You'll be left with nothing in the end,' she said quite viciously. 'Nothing.'

Again the coldness came, so paralysing that Mell seemed to be shrinking. Why should those words chill her blood and leave her with this helpless sensation of loneliness and loss? She had to struggle to force out the words, 'Aren't we all?' and then to walk steadily out of the room. As she began climbing the stairs Nanny came out of the kitchen hissing,

'I hope you haven't been upsetting her.'

Mell turned and shook her head and realised it would take very little more to have her sitting on the stairs laughing hysterically. '*Me* upset *her*? I've news for you, Nanny, my mother is the stirrer in this house.'

She shut and locked her bedroom door because she needed nobody following her in there. Then she flopped down on the stool in front of her dressing-table and let out her breath in a long deep sigh.

This had to be funny, her mother asking Barney if he intended making an honest woman of her. The last time he had been in that room Elizabeth had screeched, 'Don't touch anything,' but as he had touched her daughter she was his for life. No wonder he had tried to explain that lifelong commitment was not on the cards.

They did have an understanding. He had helped her break out of her little prison but there was no question of him staying handcuffed to her for ever. That was the last thing he expected and she had always known they would part and he would go. She had not always known how much she would miss him, this week had shown her that, but she would not have missed these last months for the world. Only she must not be too thankful. That would be cheating on the bargain.

She wished he had hung around then they could have laughed off the silly scene with her mother. He might phone or he might come back and anyway she could see him tomorrow. But she would not go over to the dig tonight because—however hard you tried to pretend that it was a hoot—it was humiliating to be put on offer again, as soon as her mother had reassessed him for hard cash. And to a man who did not even see her as a long term companion, let alone a wife. He did not see any woman as a wife. Applied to himself it was not a word in his vocabulary.

Watty was waiting, smoking his pipe in the potting shed and keeping watch through the window. When she went out to lock the van he sauntered out, head cocked enquiringly. If she didn't go over and tell him what had happened he would come up and ask, so she walked on to the sunbaked lawn and he was beside her in a trice. 'Well?'

'My mother's been asking Barney his intentions.'

The pipe, clamped between Watty's few remaining teeth, nearly fell out. He grabbed it just in time, looked blank, then disbelieving. 'She never wants you two married?'

'She doesn't want it. I think he frightens her to death. But that was what it was all about, my future.'

'What did Barney say?'

'Would you take on my family, with Nanny thrown in?'

Watty cackled then asked, 'But what about you? How do you feel about all this?'

'About Barney? He's a good friend.' She spoke lightly, she didn't want Watty deciding she was losing her heart and having a man-to-man natter with Barney in the potting shed. 'Of course I'll miss him when he goes,' she said, 'but there's nothing serious between us.'

She smiled and Watty's answering grin was relieved. 'There's others about,' he declared expansively. 'You don't have to settle for that Gunnison, there's plenty more fish in the sea.'

'Shoals of them,' Mell agreed. But if she was not careful she could end with some real heartache because it would be so easy to be in deadly earnest, wanting promises, turning possessive. And then she might see another side of Barnaby Rudd. If she let herself care too much she would deserve the pain because she knew the rules. If she tried to tie him down he would walk away and never look back . . .

'Today's the day, isn't it?' said Pammie next morning.

'Huh?' said Mell.

'Isn't he coming back today?'

Mell had mentioned that and she had not mentioned that Barney had been round to her home last night. Now she said, 'That's right,' and Pammie said,

'He hasn't phoned you here, has he? Has he rung you at home?'

I must have been grabbing the phone here, too, thought Mell, or running up from the workroom every time it rang. I must stop being so obvious. 'No he hasn't.' She shrugged as she said that and Pammie tutted sympathetically.

'*Men!* I love 'em but you can't trust 'em, it's out of sight out of mind with all of 'em. I bet he hasn't gone short of company while he's been away.'

Pain twisted inside Mell while she was smiling and protesting, 'It's nothing to do with me what he does when he's away. Ours is a no-questions-asked arrangement.'

'Well it would be,' said Pammie. 'I can't see him answering many questions.'

Mell didn't run upstairs when the phone rang during the morning. She carried on with her roller-printing and let Pammie take the calls, although she was straining to hear. When Pammie appeared at the top of the steps down to the basement she held her breath, and when Pammie asked, 'Do we have any of those butterfly jackets left that you did last year?' she couldn't have said whether she was glad or sorry. She wanted to hear from Barney but it would be awkward discussing last night with Pammie all ears.

When Pammie called, 'This is the one you've been waiting for,' Mell could have brained her, but all she could do was dash up, tugging off her dye-stained gloves, and take the call. Luckily there were two customers needing Pammie's attention so Mell turned her back, cradled the receiver against her shoulder, and kept her voice down.

'Hi!' she whispered. 'Sorry about last night,' and she heard him smiling as he said,

'I thought I'd better not hang around after that.' He hadn't taken it seriously, thank heaven.

'Watty was dead worried,' she said. 'He thought Nanny might have served you poisoned drop scones.'

'I wouldn't touch her drop scones with a bargepole.'

'Very wise,' she gurgled. 'If I were you I'd keep away. Every time you set foot in our house it's like high noon.'

'I was invited in. Mind you, it was an offer I couldn't refuse. I was talking to Watty when Nanny Demdike——'

'Demster!' She giggled again. Old Demdike was one of the Lancashire witches during the horrific witchcraft trials of the seventeenth century. 'Although I don't know,' she said. 'Do you believe in reincarnation?'

'Watty does. When he saw her coming he said, "What's the old witch after now?".' It was good to be laughing because her mother could have taken all the laughter out of their friendship. '"Mrs Beaumont wishes to see you," she said, but it sounded more like, "I've got your measure and I'm sticking the pins in".'

Mell could imagine. Seeing in this dark and powerful young man a threat to their plans Nanny would have looked grim, delivering that message. 'Did she see you out?' Mell asked.

'She popped out of the kitchen door as I was leaving. Your mother was saying what amounted to never darken my doors again, and Nanny Demdike was knocking up a spell.'

'She *what*?'

'In a small cauldron. Stirring it with a wooden spoon.'

'That was a mixing bowl and a sponge cake.'

'That was her story.'

She was so elated it was turning into a joke that she beamed from ear to ear. 'How did the week go?' she asked.

'Fine. And yours?'

'Oh I've been hard at work on some new designs I'd like to show you.' That was true. This morning's prints were run-offs of the new line. 'I'll bring some along to the dig when I shut the shop,' she said, and there was a moment's silence before he said,

'I'd like to see them. I'll be here.'

'I'll be there.'

'I bet you will,' said Pammie. She had arrived at the back of the shop again. Now she sat down in the chair behind the desk, openly listening to what Mell had to say.

'Bye then.' Mell put down the receiver and went to her workroom, picking up her gloves from the stone steps where she had dropped them, wondering if she had over-reacted about what had seemed like hesitation. Although he had laughed about last night perhaps it had started him wondering if they were seeing too much of each other. She had taken it for granted that he enjoyed being with her, and he did, but he hadn't phoned her while he was away and he hadn't said yes right away when she had said she would be over this evening.

She felt less carefree driving to Ruddington that night. Before she had been living for the moment and the moment had been great, but things were changing. She parked where she always parked, in the big yard among the other cars and motor bikes. Barney's car was there so he was about, and up to now she had always jumped out of the van and gone looking for him as if he was her only reason for coming.

The barn doors were open and Jim came out and walked across towards her. He was one of the few who had stayed on from the cutting of the first piece of turf, although there had been a steady changing stream of volunteers. Last week she would have asked him at once, 'Where's Barney?' Tonight she said 'Hallo, how's everything?' and he said, 'I was expecting you now Barney's back.'

The illusion of herself and Barney being in a charmed circle was fading; she was seeing now how she must seem to outsiders. 'I've been busy this week,' she said.

'Sure you have,' said Jim, in the same know-all tone that Pammie adopted.

'Look.' She opened the folder she was carrying and showed him the prints and the pages of sketches, based on the patterns of the mosaic. 'I thought these for T-shirts,' she pointed out a basket of flowers, 'and I've been working some of the geometrics into skirts, round the hem.'

Jim knew what she did for a living but he was not over-impressed by a talent for handprinting and sewing, although he was very impressed by Mell Beaumont. 'The girls should go for them,' he said. 'Souvenirs of the dig. A pity we're coming to the end of the season but with luck we'll be back next year.'

'Will you?'

'Barney's well in with the family. He's been coming down here since he was at Cambridge with Alan Whitehead.

'Was Barney at Cambridge? Does he have a string of degrees?'

Jim's sandy eyebrows went down and up. 'He's bloody brilliant, didn't you know that? You'd be hard pressed to find any company where he didn't have the intellectual upper hand.'

'My goodness.' She pulled a surprised face although she was not surprised.

'I'm off next Saturday,' said Jim suddenly.

'I'll miss you.' She would. He had usually worked beside her and made no secret of fancying her.

'Not like you'll miss Barney,' he said glumly.

She would miss Barney like the sun going down and never rising again but she must never admit that, and she trotted out the words that had reassured Watty. 'Of course I'll miss him when he goes, he's a good friend, but there's nothing serious between us.'

She wondered if she should print that across a T-shirt and parade around in it ... There is nothing serious between Barnaby Rudd and Amelia Beaumont, some-time known as Barney and Mell ... Or carry a banner. Or tape it on a pocket recorder so that she could flick the switch every time the subject came up.

'I didn't plan on being here more than a month,' Jim declared suddenly. 'Do you know why I stayed on?'

'Of course. The mosaic.'

'Well yes, that's the find of a lifetime. But if we'd only turned up a few lumps of stone I'd still have spent all my summer vacation here, because of you.'

She smiled. 'Get along with you.'

'Straight up. I think you're great. I know you and Barney have been living in each other's pockets ever since you met but he's a committed loner, he'll never really need anyone. But I'd like it if you and I could keep in touch. I really think we could get something going.'

She liked Jim. She liked them all. She had a list of addresses from here which might become pen-friendships or could stick at Christmas cards, and she was willing to tack Jim on to that. But she could not imagine anything developing between them that would not be like a guttering candle compared with a prairie fire after Barney.

'I think you're a knock-out,' Jim blurted out. 'You're so full of life and so pretty and sexy. Well I think you're more than pretty, you're beautiful. You've got the most beautiful hair and super legs.' He gulped so that the Adam's apple in his scraggy neck bobbed up and down.

'Thank you, I'm flattered,' Mell said, although she had never found Jim even remotely fanciable. Then she smiled and shook her head. 'But I wouldn't do for you. Under the skin I'm a bit of a bitch.'

'No you're not,' he contradicted her, and she was reminded of Robert who always knew best. 'We'll keep in touch, eh?'

'Sure,' she said. The occasional letter maybe, but that was all.

'Now I suppose you want to know where Barney is,' he said.

'No hurry.' Tonight she was not running after Barney. She asked about the dig—what another week had revealed, who was leaving this weekend. She walked towards the barn with Jim, carrying her folder.

Inside the barn the evening meal was being eaten at

the long trestle table. Four young men and three girls looked up when Mell and Jim came in. They were all students. Some had been here several weeks, three had arrived last week, but with the easy camaraderie of the dig Mell knew them all, and they all smiled at her.

'Well, I'd have won my bet if I could have got anyone to take it,' said a lanky bespectacled young man called Theo.

'What bet?' Mell asked and Theo explained,

'I was offering five to one you'd be along today now Barney's back,' and she led the laughter that followed because she had to stop them suspecting that this was any more than a summer affair for her.

'Sheer coincidence,' she said, with a look of studied innocence. 'Now can I interest anyone in my new line of dig gear?' She sat down on the end of one of the benches and cleared a small space at the end of the table for her folio. The girls asked prices and Mell gave a sales talk. These three had not seen her shop but they arranged to drive over.

'So long as you remember we're hard up,' said Sally, who had spiky dark hair and spiky dark lashes.

'I'm very cheap,' said Mell, and thought, I shall change that slogan. I am sick of it.

She heard Barney coming. She heard his footsteps although there were others and she was sitting with her back to the open doors of the barn. She heard his voice, too, although it was only at conversation pitch. She didn't turn.

Sally was describing her own attempts at tie-dying in the washer of a flat she was sharing with her boyfriend. It had been fairly successful but the next wash had turned all his underwear and shirts a muddy green. 'He went *spare*,' she shrieked. 'We'd split by the end of the week but he left all his shirts behind so I dyed 'em again and wore 'em!'

Mell laughed and felt her heartbeats quickening. When everyone else looked towards the open door and Barney she counted three slowly and silently before she turned her head and then she said cheerfully, 'Oh, hallo.'

Before they had always touched on meeting, even if it was just a hand reaching out. But tonight, although he came to stand beside her and admire the prints and the designs, they kept apart and she had a chilling premonition that they would never really touch again.

There was a flight of stylised birds winging over a skirt and a girl with a flower on a dress. All in the browns and orange and cream and sepia of the mosaic. 'If she'd thought of it sooner,' Jim chortled, 'we could all have worn T-shirts with "I dig the dig".'

'Somehow I can't see Professor Richmond in one,' said Sally. 'I would, though. Why don't you do some?'

'There's too much of a holiday camp atmosphere about this place as it is,' said Barney, and grinned. 'Why do you think we had so much trouble getting permission to carry on with the excavation?'

They all got the message. Alan was with him, smiling too, because William Whitehead, having hummed and hawed for weeks, had finally agreed that the site of the villa should be developed beyond this summer. It would be shut down and backfilled this month and opened again in the spring. An ongoing situation that could mean years of research in the meadow. That could keep Barney here and bring him back, but he wasn't looking at Mell. He was talking to the others and it was almost as though he was stressing that she was not particularly involved in this.

She listened and smiled and pretended to be surprised and thrilled. Well she was, although as Alan said it was more or less a foregone conclusion that his father would let them clear at least the mosaic floor. 'He just likes everybody to remember he's the boss. He's chuffed about it really. Barney's almost got him believing he found it and dug it out himself.'

Barney knew how to handle most things, Mell thought; he could make almost anything go his way. 'Will you all be back?' she asked.

Yes, they said, yes. 'I'll be waiting for you,' she said gaily, and wished she hadn't because it was Jim who said, 'That'll bring me.'

Then Sally said, 'We were thinking we might go round to the village hop tonight, how about it?'

It was the first Mell had heard of any plans but now Sally was asking her and Barney and Alan, looking at all three of them, and Mell asked, 'What hop?'

'In the church hall,' said Sally. 'It's for the church roof or something, isn't it?'

'They usually are,' said Mell, and Alan said hastily, 'Sorry but I can't make it.'

'Neither can I,' said Barney. 'I've brought a load of work back.'

'Mell?' said Jim.

She waited for Barney to say something but she supposed he had. He had said he had work to do and that meant he didn't need company. 'All right,' she said.

Barney and Alan went. Last week Mell would have gone with them. She would have walked beside Barney and asked what the work was, and chattered about her week because she would have been sure he wanted her with him. But now she saw how that would look to everybody. Mell, hanging on to Barney, trailing along behind him.

The last thing she wanted was to go off with the crowd. She felt more like creeping away on her own, but she was stuck for a few hours and she had to keep smiling that long.

When the table was cleared and they had carted plates and cutlery over to the outhouse, and washed and stacked them, the girls changed T-shirts for snazzy tops and old jeans for new, stripping off in the loft behind a screen of baled straw.

Mell retouched her make-up, for something to do in the middle of all the preparations. She was wearing the yellow silk dress she had worn on her birthday, and two long thin gold chains. She hadn't deliberately chosen

this dress. At least she didn't think she had, she had
worn it a lot since that night. With the tiny tear mended
so carefully that it was invisible it was a favourite with
her and she didn't have to think hard to know why.

She pulled a comb through her hair and tossed the
heavy waves back from her face and Sally said
enviously, 'Lucky thing! I wish my hair would grow like
yours.'

I'm not all that lucky, thought Mell, and what luck I
had I am paying for. Knowing that Jim was waiting at
the bottom of the ladder from the loft didn't lift her
spirits. He practically pounced on her as she stepped
from the last rung and they went off in a group,
walking the short distance from the farm to the village
green and the church hall.

All the way Jim kept close to Mell. She hadn't
minded that when they were working on the dig. She
hadn't minded when he droned on, she had only half
listened most of the time, but tonight was a social
occasion and Jim was set on monopolising her. He felt
that her time with Barney was coming to a close and he
was offering a shoulder to cry on, and she read him like
a book, but if she allowed herself the luxury of tears she
would do it alone.

She was as blithe as any of them, walking through
the village towards the sound of music, joking and
fooling as they joined the small queue buying tickets
just inside the hall, where a very young local group was
on the stage, belting out a request from the top of the
pops.

It was an unpretentious affair, with a bar and a
buffet, proceeds to the church restoration fund, but it
was jolly. Nearly everyone knew everyone else. Mell,
from another village, only recognised the occasional
face, but they were all welcomed by the vicar, oozing
bonhomie, and his slender smiling wife.

Mell met Susan James, whom she had phoned about
the Cupid. Susan didn't know that. She was selling
raffle tickets and got them as they settled into a corner

at the back of the hall. She said, 'Barney isn't coming I suppose?' as soon as she had said hallo.

'Hallo, young Susan,' said Jim. 'No he isn't, and this is Mell.'

Susan's head whirled and Mell found herself smiling stiffly under the scrutiny of sharp young eyes. Susan James was in orange jeans and a pink polka-dot shirt that matched her pink fringe. She was about fourteen and she took in Mell's appearance with a wry smile and then said, 'Anybody for a raffle ticket?'

Poor kid, thought Mell, she has a crush on Barney. If he's been coming to the village ever since he was an undergraduate that could have started when she was a babe in arms. She felt an affinity with Susan; she could imagine herself as a child making a dream hero out of the strong and handsome young man who laughed easily and made everything exciting. Come to that she had done. Only Mell was a woman when Barney crossed her path and the dreams had spilled into real life and that was where the danger lay.

They bought tickets and Susan moved on but later, when Mell was walking along the buffet table, spearing the odd sausage roll and slice of pie, Susan stepped up beside her and said, 'It's super about the villa, isn't it?'

'Isn't it just?' Susan had probably been along to the dig during the day, it would have been easy for Mell to miss her. She hovered when they reached the end of the table to ask,

'Have you met Gemma?'

'Once,' said Mell, and this time Susan's little smile said, Poor you, you don't have any more chance than I do!

The vocalist, a fair-haired willowy lad who looked around seventeen, and who had been reading out requests and messages and urging dancers on to the floor, suddenly said, 'And this is my own request, I'm singing this for Susan.' Clutching the microphone he began to sing a throbbing ballad and cheers went up from the youngsters who knew what this was about.

Susan blushed hotly up to her pink fringe. 'Oh hell,' spluttered the vicar's daughter. 'I can't stand immature men.'

Mell found the dancing almost a therapy. She had never thought of herself as a dancer. She had gone to dances with partners like Robert, with whom she had danced sedately, keeping in step with their steps. But tonight she danced alone. Oh, she got up with Jim usually, and with others who asked her, but she moved with the beat rather than with the men. She had shed a lot of inhibitions this summer, she didn't care now who watched her as she turned and twirled.

When the group played a smoochy waltz Jim held out his arms to her and she said, 'I'll trample your feet, I'm no good at the close-up stuff,' and swayed away, dancing alone although he was on the floor with her. In fact she never trod on feet, she had had plenty of practise in the traditional waltz, but she did not want Jim's arms around her. Nor anybody's here.

But she danced most of the dances and the rest of the time she chatted and joked. When the raffle tickets were drawn the first prize of a large bottle of whisky was won by an elderly lady who shot up on to the platform on thin little legs to collect her prize. Somebody called, 'It's a fiddle,' and laughter rippled through the hall, and a woman sitting near Mell explained 'She's eighty-nine and she usually seems to win the raffle if it's a bottle.'

Mell laughed, too, her bright hair spilling over her flushed face, and Jim leaned across and stroked her cheek and ran his fingers under the V-neck of her dress, tracing her cleavage, and she nearly spat at him, 'Don't maul me,' which would have put a damper on the party. When he said good night he was surely going to kiss her. He might try more, but a clutch and a kiss were inevitable and it was time for her to leave.

Jim had drunk several pints of the local beer, which was making him even more amorous, and when he went to the bar for another round she whispered to Sally,

'I'm going to slip away. Cover for me for a few minutes, I don't want Jim haring after me.'

Sally said sure, and Mell crept out of the hall, and ran through the empty village back to the farm and her van. The air was cool. The sultry summer was over and cloud shapes drifted across the sky. There were lights on in the farmhouse but the barn was dark; the barn crowd were all at the church hall. Barney could be anywhere: in the farm, in the boathouse. She backed her van out of the row of cars and bikes to swing it round, but instead of driving down the farm track on to the road she tucked herself under some trees well away from her original parking place, where no one would spot the van unless they looked for it.

She hoped Jim would presume she was gone. Perhaps she should be gone, but what harm could it do to walk along to the boathouse? If Barney was working he was surely due to finish by now, and surely she could just look in and say, 'Hey, you want to hear what you missed?'

By the time she had crossed the rough grass of the first meadow to reach the towpath her eyes should have been growing accustomed to the dim light, but strangely the night seemed to be getting darker. The clouds must be thickening. Trees and hedges formed solid walls of shadow and once the water had foamed over the weir, it ran like black pitch. She went quickly, almost running, until she saw the light from the boathouse.

She heard a typewriter and wondered what he was typing. She could be interrupting work and if she was she would say, 'I only looked in to say good night,' and pretty silly that would sound. But she had to climb the wooden steps and tap on the door because he might say, 'I hoped you'd come.'

He said, 'Come in,' and he hadn't been waiting for her because he looked at her for a moment with a sigh and frowned as he sat back. There were papers on the table, notes and typing. 'What time is it?' He answered himself, looking at his watch. 'Ah well,' he said, 'and how was the village hop?'

'Very friendly.' She closed the door behind her and noticed how tired he looked. She had never seen him look so tired before, his energy had always seemed to be boundless. She longed to stroke his temples or go and stand behind him and knead the knotted muscles in his neck and back. She said, 'I've never seen you working before. Well, out on the dig of course but——'

'But this is what keeps the wolf from the door.' When he grinned he began to look better, although the furrows across his forehead were still deep.

'Could I scrounge a cup of coffee?' she asked. 'Could I make you one?'

'Sit down, I can use the exercise.' He got up, pausing to flex his shoulders as though he had been pouring over papers for hours, and went into the kitchenette. She perched on the edge of the little blue settee feeling foolishly shy because she couldn't think of anything worth saying.

At last she said, 'I'm glad you've got permission to carry on.'

'It's a superb floor. Puts his grazing land a cut above average and there's still plenty left for the cows.'

'You'll come back?'

'I don't know.' There would be government grants now for a listed site but they would never have found the villa at all if Alan had not mentioned that shadowy outline to Barney. Surely Barney would want to be here when they uncovered more of it next summer. It was almost his villa.

'But you have to be here,' she said tautly and he laughed,

'I don't have to be anywhere. That's the joy of being a hobo.'

He was promising nothing and she asked, 'Where are you going from here?'

'I've got a boat in a boatyard in Corfu. I'm taking it round some islands.'

'Not the *Misty*?' That was a silly thing to say when the *Misty* was still under the willow trees.

'The *Cormorant*,' he said. 'An ocean-goer.'

'Need a deckhand?' She laughed and he shook his head smiling but a visa of islands swam in her head and she longed for the wide world that was out there. She said, 'Send me postcards?'

'All right.' She would come downstairs and find them on the mat, coloured pictures that she could dream around.

'Can I write to you?'

'Of course.'

'Where shall I write?'

He had to think about that. 'Well,' she said, 'leave me some addresses when you go. I'm collecting addresses. Do you know why Jim Boulton stayed on here?'

He was pouring boiling water over coffee granules. 'Has he been telling you why?'

'The mosaic's lovely, he says, but it doesn't have my legs.'

Barney laughed. 'A bit stubby, the mosaic girls. And what shall you do about Jim?'

'Keep in touch, why not? Susan was disappointed you weren't with us tonight. She's another of your fans. Don't forget to send her some postcards. There must be girls all over the place waiting to hear from you.'

He brought the coffee and the mug was so hot that she put it down quickly and said, 'It's been an interesting summer, I'm sorry it's over.'

'Summers have a knack of ending,' he said.

'Well, it was fun.' She still could not imagine the winter without him but the thought of it made her shiver, and she began to tell him about the village hop, exaggerating the zany bits: lucky old Mrs Spriggs who always won the whisky, and the boy who sang for Susan who couldn't stand immature men.

'I had my money's worth,' she said. 'I enjoyed it. You should have come.'

'I'm not much of a dancer.'

She smiled at him. Of course he could dance. His

body was so well co-ordinated that with a little practice
he could probably have mastered any routine, but they
had never danced together. 'Well I am a fantastic
mover,' she said, airily and untruthfully. 'My body
language has to be seen to be believed. That is
something I could have taught you if we'd thought
about it earlier.'

She got up and turned on the radio, laughing at him.
'Fair's fair,' she said. 'I've learned some fascinating
moves from you this summer. Let me show you how to
dance. Come on, on your feet.' She snapped fingers and
swayed, did a few twirls and held out her hands to him.
When he stood up she touched his fingertips and the
current went through her so that she felt that the ends
of her hair should be shooting sparks.

She kept a set smile on her lips but he must have seen
the turmoil in her eyes because he stood still, then he
said, 'You must go home.'

He knew·what she was doing. She was hoping to
make him laugh and hold her, one thing leading to
another until they ended in the warmth and closeness of
the little bed. But he did not want her clinging to him
any longer. She was yesterday's girl and she would
never reach for him again. She said, 'You are so right, I
must go. Any time now Nanny could fly past that
window on her broomstick.' She hadn't clung to him.
She had let go smiling. 'It doesn't have to be a full
moon,' she said. 'My old nanny's an all-weather witch.'

Barney walked with her back to the van. A fine
drizzle of rain had started and it was so dark that she
stood blinking at the top of the wooden steps and then
came down very carefully, using the rail. He went just
ahead of her so that if she had stumbled she would have
fallen against him. But she watched that she did not
stumble and walking along the towpath she kept her
arms folded tightly, babbling away. 'What's this boat
like? The *Cormorant*. That's a bird isn't it?'

Of course cormorants were birds, she knew that, but
as she knew nothing about boats she wasn't much wiser

when he told her, 'It's a thirty-three foot ketch, thirty-seven horse power.'

'Where will you be going?' she asked in chatty tones. 'Tell me the names of some of the islands.'

'Patmos, Lipsos, Leros, Lakki.' They meant nothing to her. They sounded like a child's doggerel verse.

'Don't forget the postcards,' she said. 'Some Greek ruins would be nice. I'll keep an eye on the villa for you. When it's covered over I'll come back from time to time and tell the girls down there that they're not forgotten. They're going to be let out again in the spring.'

'I'm sure they'll appreciate that,' said Barney and she thought, what drivel I am talking; and shut up until they reached the spot where she had parked her van.

She got in quickly calling, 'Good night.' She did not want the others flagging her down, asking why she had cleared off, knowing she had gone to Barney. She half expected Jim to jump out of the shadows when she switched on her headlights but she got down the track and away without seeing anyone else.

At home her mother's bedroom had the only light burning. The door was ajar and as Mell climbed the stairs her mother called, 'Amelia, is that you?'

'Of course.'

'Are you all right?'

'Yes of course.'

'Where have you been?'

Mell looked into the room. Elizabeth was in bed, with pillows piled behind her and an open magazine. 'I went to a dance,' said Mell. Elizabeth bit on her lip and Mell said, 'With most of them but not with Barney.'

'I'm sorry.' Elizabeth looked woeful, then almost gleeful. 'No I'm not. You know I don't like him, I don't like you seeing him, so it's no use pretending I do.'

'No use at all,' said Mell. 'They're all packing up soon and he doesn't seem anxious to leave me a forwarding address so you don't have much to worry about.'

Elizabeth smiled sweetly and wished Mell good night

and said, 'Sleep well.' Her mother would sleep well, Mell felt, and she shut herself in her bedroom, closing her door softly although she would have liked to slam it so that the whole house shook.

She wanted to shout, 'I won't be left behind,' but making a fuss would change nothing; the china cat, perched on the dressing table, seemed to be leering at her. 'And you can stop smirking,' she said, and shoved it aside with the back of her hand, so that it toppled off the edge, landing on a carpet that had worn thin over the years and smashing into several pieces.

She let it lie. It seemed to sum up the situation. The cat was broken, the weather was breaking, and the way she felt now she was falling apart herself . . .

CHAPTER NINE

AT last Mell picked up the fragments of the china cat and dropped them in the bottom drawer of the dressing-table, although there was no sense in keeping it, she would never mend it. The head still grinned its silly grin, and she took off the two gilt chains she wore and then the yellow dress and dropped them in the drawer, too. When she was stronger she would get rid of all this, reminders she did not need.

She had always known that the parting would come. The long goodbye could last another couple of weeks, although they had really said goodbye tonight, when she had wanted to stay and he had told her to go. She wanted him terribly, physically. Without his touch she felt she could wither and fade like a plant without water or light. And to the end of her life she would miss his mind, his laugh, the vitality that made every other man seem colourless.

She wanted to go with him, but he always moved on alone and maybe Mell had not changed so much after all because she still shrank from creating a scene. There was no point anyway. She would sound pathetic if she told Barney, 'All that talk about no strings was rubbish from the start, because I have been falling in love with you from the first day and I want us to spend the rest of our lives together.'

'Sorry, sweetheart,' he would say, 'but that wasn't part of the bargain.' So it was better to part friends, leave him liking her, maybe coming back next year. That was the only way, but right now it offered more misery than joy, and she daren't even cry herself to sleep; Pammie would notice if she had red eyes at the boot fair and if the rain persisted sunglasses would be out. But she lay a long time, still and quiet, and next morning she could hardly have felt more drained and exhausted if she had not slept at all.

Nanny was hobbling round the kitchen, complaining about her arthritis. 'It's this weather,' she said, shaking two painkillers out of the bottle, and Mell thought, I could use a few of those. Although what she was feeling was less pain than emptiness. Nothing that was going to stop her operating efficiently, looking and sounding fine, but just this aching hollow inside.

'You were over there last night, I suppose,' said Nanny, and Mell said,

'Yes, but it's packing-up time from now on, then the dig's closing and they're all going away.'

Nanny breathed a deep sigh of silent thanks then she said softly, 'He wouldn't have done. He wasn't the right one.'

'He never thought he was,' said Mell. She was the one who had wanted the closeness to last for ever, because it had seemed so right to her.

Today there were fewer stalls at the boot fair, and fewer customers. Plastic sheets were laid over displays and those who had awnings had most of their goods under cover. It was not the weather for summer clothing and trade at the Rainbow's End site was sluggish. This should have been drag-racing Sunday but that was rained off by midday and Pammie's Graham, and Alec Wilson, came down to shelter under the awning, bringing coffee and hot dogs from the refreshments van.

Their idea was that the girls should pack up and they should all four clear off for the rest of the day together. Pammie was all for it, nobody was buying and stock was getting damp, and Mell agreed that this was a waste of time but she did not want to join the party. She said, 'We might as well pack up, but I must get home.'

'Got a date?' asked Alec.

'Visitors this evening.' Well, it was an easy excuse.

'Another time?'

She smiled. 'Yes, why not?'

Jim came up as they lifted boxes into the van and said, 'Glad I caught you. Where are you going from here?'

'Home,' said Mell.

'Had a bit of a thick head this morning; that local brew's pretty potent,' said Jim, 'but I thought I'd come and see if you were at a loose end.'

'No,' said Mell. She eased in the bag with the awning struts and Pammie muttered, 'They're like bees round a honeypot round you these days, aren't they?'

Mell smiled ruefully. 'I'm no honeypot.' But she need not be lonely. She seemed to attract men now without even trying, and there had to be some around who had plenty to recommend them, but she would never hear her name linked with anybody without wanting to say, 'You should have seen the one that got away.'

She left Jim and Alec with Pammie and Graham and went to the shop and unloaded. The high season of tourist trade was ending and in a little while there was no reason why she should not take a break. She could shut the shop, or ask Anna if she would take over for a few weeks. She had to have something to look forward to or the grey days ahead might become too depressing to face. I shall do that, she thought, and it was a comforting secret she would keep to herself for now.

During the last two weeks they cleared no more on the dig. With the future of the villa assured there was no longer any urgency and effort was concentrated on covering and protecting, and collating the records and photographs and finds of this season's excavation.

Barney was in the thick of it. He always had been, of course, but Mell was realising now that after Professor Richmond he was probably the most knowledgeable expert here. He was brilliant. He was a top man. She was glad he was her friend, and she would read his articles, his books, get news of him. She would follow his career from now, through others if he forgot to write because, of course, he was not tied to her in any way.

They met, they talked, they ate meals together, but not alone. Now there were always the others around, and they all knew exactly what they would be doing when they left here. When the dig closed down the students were back to their polys and colleges, and the seniors to their various professional niches.

Barney was envied because he was sailing round the Greek islands while he got this book together, flying out the day after he left here, and who could blame him if he was anxious to be gone? This project was in abeyance, nothing new or exciting would be turned up here although there was still work to be done.

Even with so little time left there were days when Mell neither saw Barney nor spoke to him. She suspected if she hadn't turned up at the dig he might not have contacted her until it was very near that last day. It was as if he was already sailing away and out of reach and she was proud of the way she was handling the situation.

She had it exactly right. Ask too much and she would be left with nothing, not even friendship, so she would ask for nothing. But she had the Bath address from which letters would be forwarded and she would write him letters that would make him smile and remember her. In October he would be on the island of Karpathos, for the wedding of a friend. She had the name of the taverna that was run by the groom and his parents and she would send a letter to Barney there. She would keep in touch, playing it oh so light and casual, but it would not be her fault if he forgot her.

At home life was easier than it had been since that first Sunday at the boot fair. Nanny and her mother were both acting as if they couldn't quite believe that Mell's rebellion was over and were scared that a word out of place might send her rushing after Barney again.

She saw Jim around the site until he left at the end of the first week, and she managed to keep out of his clutches without hurting his feelings. She wrote down his address and he knew hers and she said, 'Thank you for taking me on as a very raw recruit, I learned a lot from you.'

'Not what I'd like to teach you,' said Jim fervently, breathing heavily. They were in the courtyard, walking towards her van, on his last night. She had only seen Barney briefly this evening; he was in conference now in the little white van that was the office, with the professor and two other men.

Mell had ended up in the barn with the students, and now she was going home. And early in the morning so was Jim, and the idea of him teaching her anything along the lines he had in mind made her smile wryly in the darkness.

'Well, goodbye,' she said, and he grabbed her and kissed her, so that she got a rather revolting mouthful of whiskers. It wasn't difficult to get away from him. He felt stiff and awkward and when she stepped back she was out of his hold. 'Good luck,' she said gently, 'and it was a lovely summer.'

'Do you think——?' he began, speaking through the slightly open window, and she waited, fingers on the ignition key. 'Do you think I ought to shave off my beard?'

Not with your chin, she thought. 'Oh no,' she said, 'it makes you look very distinguished,' and at her last sight of him he was stroking his beard and smiling . . .

The next week passed much as the last had done. At home she felt that her mother was counting the days until Barney was out of the country. She asked about Mell's plans quite anxiously. 'Will you be coming straight home?' when Mell took up the morning tea, and it was usually yes, because Mell didn't hurry over to the dig now although she sometimes went along later.

And more often than not Elizabeth was waiting when Mell got back, with a concern that might have been touching if Mell had not been keeping a check on her own emotions. She could not allow herself to weaken. She needed the coldness within herself like an anaesthetic. Without it the pain could start.

The last day was a Saturday. In the meadow the dig had been refilled with protective layering although it was still marked out and fenced off. The site office and the 'finds' tent had been taken away, and a get-together of everyone who had worked on the dig and could get here was planned for Saturday night.

William Whitehead, who considered himself the hero of the hour, was hosting a party in the drawing room and dining room of the huge old farmhouse. After that it was all over until next spring, but it seemed fitting that such a successful season should close with a bang.

It was to be a dress-up affair and Mell considered wearing the yellow silk dress, but so briefly that she did not even take it out of the drawer although this would be her last evening with Barney. What she would do was wear the waterfall earrings and be very lighthearted and sparkling, because it was a party and a reunion. Jim couldn't get back—which was something to be thankful for—but some who had come and gone would be there and it would be fun to see them all. After tonight it would be a long time before she took the familiar road to the dig again.

She spent Saturday morning in her workroom, organising autumn stock and deciding what she would wear for the party. Maybe a long skirt with a plain blouse and a fringed shawl. There were some dramatic shawls and she was going through a pile of them when she heard the footsteps on the stone steps.

Customers who knew her often popped down here, to chat, to watch her at work, to go through stock, and she turned with a smile that felt as if it was stitched to her face when she saw Gemma.

Gemma was smiling all the way down and right until she was standing beside Mell. Even with her lips closed over the small white teeth her face was still alight with mockery. 'You look better than when I saw you last,' she said.

Mell had just come out of the river that night, but it wasn't just that the bedraggled hair was glossy and

bouncing today. The change was more fundamental
than that. Mell had bloomed this summer so that she
was almost beautiful and she had confidence enough to
say, 'You're looking quite spectacular, but then I'm
sure you always do.'

'Of course,' said Gemma. She still wore her hair in a
thick red plait falling to her waist. Her skin was a
flawless matt and with her perfect features and almost
anorexic slimness she could have been a model out of
the window of a fashionable store. A walking, talking
doll, thought Mell. Susan James is right, I don't know
any girl who could give Gemma any competition.

She asked, 'What can I do for you?' and Gemma said,
'They tell me you've designed some clothes with
patterns from the mosaic floor. I've come to see if
there's anything I could wear for this party tonight.'

Gemma had done no work on the dig and Mell
would have heard—from Jim if no one else—if she had
come down again after that early visit, but she would
probably be the hit of the evening. Although Mell very
much doubted if it would be in anything from
Rainbow's End, and when she produced a few garments
Gemma's expression said she wouldn't be seen dead in
any of them.

'Not really you, are they?' said Mell. 'So what else
can I do for you?' She didn't believe for a minute that
Gemma's reason for coming here was to choose a cheap
and cheerful outfit. She was prowling around now like a
disdainful cat, eyeing the merchandise, eyeing Mell.
'Nothing really,' she said, and then, 'you're coming
tonight, I suppose?'

'Yes.' Although if she had known earlier that Gemma
would be there she might have made some excuse.
Gemma picked up a scarf with mosaic flowers running
along it and wrinkled her nose.

'I'm sure it's all madly exciting,' she said, 'but one
mosaic looks much the same as another to me.'

'Is that why you haven't been to see it?' asked Mell
and Gemma drawled,

'I've been *busy*, but I have kept up to date on everything that's been going on.' Her feline smile was knowing. 'Don't blush,' she said. Mell didn't realise she was blushing; if anything, she thought she might be getting paler as Gemma went on, 'Barney and I go our own ways a lot of the time. I've certainly had my moments this summer and I know that he has.' She laughed silently. 'It's something amusing to talk about when we do get together.'

Jim had said that Gemma tried to make Barney jealous and she probably had some steamy tales to tell, but Barney would not talk about Mell. Somebody had but not Barney. No way. All the same Mell had to fight to keep her self-control when she wanted to say, 'You're a liar, he wouldn't.'

'Sailing round the islands,' said Gemma dreamily. 'He never comes back for anybody so I make sure I'm there. It should be quite a trip.'

'You should be there more often,' said Mell. 'It was quite a summer.'

'Everything all right?' Pammie called down the stairs and Mell nearly called back, 'You've missed the best bits.'

'Yes thank you,' she did say, and, to Gemma, 'Sorry you couldn't find anything you like. I'll see you this evening.'

Pammie watched her go with awe, asking as soon as the shop door shut, 'Who was that? She just asked for you. I thought she looked a bit familiar. She's a dazzler isn't she? Is she an actress?'

'A model,' said Mell, 'so you could have seen her.'

Pammie's 'Ah!' was impressed.

'She's also a good friend of Barney's,' said Mell.

'Ah,' said Pammie on a different note. 'Well, she is a bit scraggy . . .'

The party was well away when Mell arrived. It was supposed to start at eight o'clock and she drove into the courtyard, that looked like a parking lot with so many cars packed in, a few minutes after eight, but lights were on in all the windows of the farmhouse and music and voices filled the air.

There couldn't be many who hadn't come back for this. Even the ones who had just done a few hours on the dig were sharing the last night and celebrating the find of the mosaic floor.

Tonight you entered through the front door and stepped into the wide panelled hall. That seemed crowded already, and so did the rooms leading off. Sylvia grabbed Mell with a delighted yell. 'Don't you look splendid? I hardly recognised you.'

Mell's dress was simple enough, another from the silk collection in the shop, this time in misty blue, but she had taken her hair up with a few tendrils falling, and she was wearing her mother's beautiful eighteenth-century earrings.

She had come downstairs in the paste waterfalls and Elizabeth had asked, 'Where did you get those?' and Mell had told her, 'Barney gave them to me.'

'Wait a minute.' Elizabeth brought down one of her jewel boxes and for the first time seemed anxious that her daughter should wear her treasures.

Mell had protested that she was all right but the earrings were exquisite, and she put them in to please her mother and thought she might change back into the paste pair before she joined the party. But she hadn't, and even Gemma wouldn't upstage her in earrings tonight.

Sylvia was telling her about the Camargue, where she and Dave had been since they moved on from the dig. Almost every face was familiar, and Mell went around catching up with everybody's news.

She saw Barney when she glanced through the first door opening into the hall. He was over by the fireplace, taller than anyone else, and as always he seemed to be the centre of the crowd. In dark jacket and white lawn shirt he looked elegant and civilised enough to impress even her mother, but as Mell looked

across at him and his eyes met hers there was nothing
civilised about her own response. That was primal. She
wanted to get to him, pushing her way through them
all. If Gemma had not been hanging around she might
have done, but she was not making a fool of herself on
this last night in front of everybody from the dig. And
she could easily become ridiculous, especially under
Gemma's darts of malice.

Later she would talk to Barney. Everybody was in
constant motion; she would come up against him, but
she mustn't shove to get to him, so she moved past the
doorway and recognised someone else and hurried to
join them.

Gemma was wearing something that looked like
golden rain: a hip-length tunic and pants caught in
around the ankles. The tunic was in narrow strips of
gold and silver and she might have been wearing a body
stocking underneath but it was hard to be sure. Mell
saw her, darting and flashing, and was asked more than
once, 'Do you know who that is?'

The first time she said, 'She's with Barney,' and as
this was to someone who had been around when Mell
had been with Barney most evenings she embarrassed
the asker. After that she shrugged and said, 'Haven't a
clue.'

It was a good party. The Whiteheads were good
hosts. The buffet filled an immense dining-table, with
country fare of cooked meats and rich pies and pastries,
salads and crudities, interspersed with gateaux and
quiches and all manner of sweets and savouries. Mrs
Whitehead and Alan's fiancée, a farmer's daughter,
knew how to put on a spread and with a blank cheque
from father had gone to town.

Everybody was enjoying it. The punch was delicious
and potent and the massive carved Victorian sideboard
was loaded with bottles, but Mell kept a glass of white
wine in her hand. She had to drive home and she had to
stay sober and sensible, although she really didn't realise
that she was avoiding Barney until he cornered her.

She had kept on the move ever since she arrived, stopping to go into huddles occasionally, but keeping well away from Gemma and dodging when she saw Barney. It was easy enough, there was always someone else to talk to. She reached Frank Simpson at the far end of the conservatory, still holding her half-filled glass, and said, 'Hallo, how lovely to see you again,' and chatted to him until Barney touched her shoulder, sending the old familiar shock of sweet fire coursing through her veins, and she knew it was time to go.

She had had to come, she had wanted to she thought, but she couldn't have swallowed a mouthful of food, and the clamour in here was deafening. She said, 'My goodness, aren't they giving you a send-off? Isn't he doing you proud after making you sweat about whether he'd let you uncover his floor?'

Frank said something and moved away so that she was standing, pressed up against a stone shelf, and Barney was looming over her. 'You can't beat the real thing, can you?' he said, and he touched an earring and she jerked her head sidewards and away. 'They're very beautiful.'

'Yes.' They were, and there was so much she should be saying, like, 'You won't talk about me will you?' or, 'You will remember me,' or, 'I shall miss you.'

Once they had seemed alone to her, even among crowds, but tonight she was conscious of every voice and every face, and she had to make light talk because everybody could hear. She kept walking while she was talking. 'I hate goodbyes but it's been nice knowing you,' and that was the understatement of a lifetime. 'Come back next spring,' she said, 'and don't forget to write.'

He said, 'Don't let them push you,' and she thought, that's fine for you. Nobody is going to push you and you probably wouldn't notice if they did.

'Nothing will happen to me that I don't want to happen,' she said and half believed what she was saying, and she saw Gemma coming and she moved faster, looking towards another group. 'I must have a word with Sally.'

'Take care,' said Barney.

'You bet,' she said. 'And you.' And she got out of the conservatory, threading her way through the partygoers and quietly through the first door that led out of the house.

The light was on in her mother's bedroom and this surely had to be Elizabeth's last night vigil. From now on there wouldn't be much danger in the company Mell was keeping. 'Amelia,' Elizabeth called as Mell climbed the stairs, and she went to the open doorway. 'Good party?' asked Elizabeth.

'No expense spared,' said Mell.

'Did you—say goodbye to everybody?'

'Barney? Yes.'

'He's really gone?'

'He'll be gone by morning,' said Mell, and Elizabeth's anxious eyes irritated her. 'What's the matter with you? What have you been expecting him to *do*?'

'He frightens me,' whispered Elizabeth. 'There's something about him.'

There was no denying that. 'He can frighten people,' Mell admitted wryly, but all that frightened her was being without him. She closed her mother's door and went downstairs and poured herself a stiff brandy. She drank that before she lay back on the pillow and it spread leadenlike through her so that she soon sank into heavy sleep.

She woke with a headache but at least she woke too late to do anything crazy, like driving back last night to see Barney again before he went and saying, 'Take me with you. I know that Gemma's going but you are going to get very bored with her and with luck she'll find an even bigger boat to hop on to . . .'

'Was it a good party?' Pammie asked as soon as she arrived at the boot fair. Mell was setting up stall and Pammie bustled to help, showing unusual consideration.

'A *very* good party,' said Mell very brightly, and for once Pammie showed some tact and asked no more.

The hang-gliders were out and an occasional light plane, and Mell could not help looking up at the planes. Barney was flying to Corfu today, not on anything like these of course, but being carried away, and that was bad enough. But thinking of Gemma sitting beside him brought a pain so intense that Pammie's temporary tactfulness deserted her and she said bluntly, 'You look *awful*.'

'Thanks a lot,' said Mell.

'It is all over, is it?' Pammie couldn't resist asking.

'Oh yes,' said Mell. She went towards the back of the awning and began to rearrange some dresses that were hanging there, and Pammie followed her to say quietly,

'I am sorry.' Dear Pammie, thought Mell, I believe you are; and she smiled fairly steadily.

'I thought you couldn't stand him.'

'Couldn't I just have done, given half a chance,' said Pammie and Mell had to laugh and, encouraged, Pammie asked, 'Will you take up with Robert again?' That was such a ridiculous question but Pammie went on, 'Well, he's got the money, he could give you things.'

'Nothing that I want,' said Mell, and after a moment Pammie said,

'No, I suppose not . . .'

'Bloody hell!' said Mell when she saw Robert's car outside her house. So far as she knew he had not been here in the last two weeks and surely her mother should know by now that Mell was never going to wear that ring. But here he was, back on the very first day she was alone.

She was not going through all that again, and she jumped out of the van and strode into the house, straight for the lounge. Robert was there, in the usual chair, holding a glass of dry sherry. He smiled when he saw her and said, 'Your mother's——'

Elizabeth was not in the room but there were two

glasses and she was obviously in the house, and Mell said, 'I'm glad I caught you on your own. I've got a suggestion for you.' This had just come into her mind and she liked it. 'Why don't you marry my mother?'

Robert did not spill his sherry and he only looked slightly surprised. Then he asked, 'Do you think she'd have me?'

'I think you stand a very good chance,' said Mell. 'Of course you'd look after Nanny?'

'Of course.'

'Then you have my blessing,' she told him gravely and got to her own room before she started to smile. The more she thought about it the more obvious it seemed. Her mother would be a Mrs Gunnison that Robert could be proud of and if Barney had still been here she would have had someone to share the joke.

It might take time before Elizabeth adjusted to the subtle shifting of Robert's objective, although he might as well have been courting her mother all the time he had been coming to this house. They had always been much more buddy-buddy than he and Mell could ever be, and Mell couldn't imagine why she hadn't thought of it sooner.

When she went downstairs again Elizabeth was listening closely to what Robert was saying and for a moment Mell wondered if he was proposing. He wasn't. He was explaining something in today's news and Elizabeth was hanging on his words, which was exactly how she liked it.

Elizabeth looked up at Mell with a warning glint in her eyes and Mell smiled and said, 'Hallo, Robert' as though this was the first time she had spoken to him, and he said, 'Good evening, Amelia,' pleased with their little secret.

Robert stayed for a meal and then Elizabeth played some of his favourite pieces on the piano, and when Mell went out of the room nobody noticed. Her mother was a skilful player but she couldn't sit there quietly, listening to the music, or she might start thinking, he's gone, it's over, and grief could overwhelm her. She could just imagine the reaction of these two if she put down her head and howled.

She went out into the garden where the night was damp and dark, walking across the lawn, past Watty's potting shed, through the arch in the beech hedge into the rose garden. The scent was faint, like a memory of perfume, and she sniffed a full blown Red Devil. The dark red blooms looked midnight black and the rain on the petals felt like tears on her face. But there were tears and she was ashamed of herself, out here, snivelling at the bottom of the garden.

It was too late for tears. It was too late for anything. She might have stood up to Gemma last night, instead of leaving the field clear. She might have talked to Barney. He cared about her. He knew the old stifling life was waiting for her if she was not very careful and she could have said, 'Stay on my side, I still need your help.'

Maybe she would write to him and say it. She would send her letter to the taverna on the island and pray that Gemma would not see it. She went back into the house, up to her room, and began to write a letter.

Every day that week she wrote. She carried the pad in her bag and it helped her, even if no one but herself would read it. It was the first love letter she had ever written and in the end she could lack the courage to post it.

She talked to Barney, telling him anything that might amuse or interest him—from Robert, likely to turn up with his mother's jewellery for Mell's mother any time now, to a colour change she was considering for the shop's décor, from white to pale coral which would be warmer for winter.

And she wrote how she missed him, pouring out her longings and her hunger. She wrote from the heart, of love. They had never spoken of love but she did now when she woke in the night, turned on the bedside lamp and imagined he was with her, and wrote the words she had never been able to say.

She wasn't looking for postcards yet, it was too soon, although Watty kept asking her, 'Heard anything from Barney?' Each day she said no and on Friday evening, when she got back from work, Watty said, 'That Gunnison's here again.'

'It could be Nanny's cooking,' said Mell. 'Maybe he's got his eye on Nanny.'

'He's an old stick-in-the-mud,' Watty grumbled.

'Oh, he's not so bad.' Mell bit on a smile. 'I'm starting to see him in a new light.'

She was tempted to confide in Watty but he could have found Mell's matchmaking so hilarious that he wouldn't be able to resist dropping broad hints to Nanny. 'Got a minute, have you?' said Watty. Without waiting for her answer he plodded off towards the potting shed and she followed on his heels.

Inside he said, 'Sit down,' and she sat down on the bench without a word because the face he turned towards her was so grim that it could have been a stranger's. 'What happened to your father mustn't happen to you,' he said.

CHAPTER TEN

It was like a little clubhouse in here. There were tin mugs and a couple of old saucers used as ashtrays between the trays of cuttings, and two cider bottles up the corner. Watty's mates came in here, and he looked towards the cider bottles as if he needed something, and Mell wondered if she should say, 'Have a drink, I can wait.'

She was not sure she wanted to hear what he was going to tell her. He was going to open a can of worms and she doubted if she would be happier afterwards. All that had happened to her father that she could remember was the car crash. She couldn't really remember him at all.

Watty sat down beside her but he didn't look at her. He said, 'Your mother's a real lady, I've got great respect for your mother, but she's selfish. Always been selfish. Always self first. She was a lovely girl; they were cousins you know——' Of course she knew. 'She lived in the big house. She was an orphan, she'd got no money of her own, but she'd always got your father. Right from when they were children she'd got your father. She was a lovely girl but she wasn't strong and he always looked after her. Nanny Demster nursed her back from the grave when she had the fever.'

Rheumatic fever that left her with the heart murmur. Mell had heard all this but Watty was seeing it again, because he had been around in those days. He was looking out into this garden and seeing another, peopled with ghosts, as he went on with his story.

'Your grandfather died and they got married and your mother was in her element, she's always been the lady. But he wanted to be an artist, John did, and she wasn't having that. It was supposed to be a hobby, he

177

had the studio down the garden, but that was what he liked doing and she wasn't having it. She wanted him where he was, not going off painting. And she stopped him.'

Watty said that with a dreadful finality and Mell gasped softly and he turned his head and began to plead with her. 'You always seemed content enough, although she'd got you tied to her all ways; but these last months you've been a different girl and it would be wicked if you went back to waiting on her and having no life of your own. She spoiled it for him. You didn't even know your father was a painter, did you?'

'I've got some of his pictures,' she said, and Watty's jaw sagged.

'You can't have. There were none of 'em left.' He was back again in his memories. 'He wanted to take six months off and paint, see if he could make something of it. They were young, still in their twenties, he wanted to take a chance.'

. . . 'In six months' time you'll have nothing, *nothing*' . . . The words, in her mother's voice, echoed in Mell's mind, spiralling in on her, and with them came that feeling of being very small and paralysed with terror.

Now a scene was forming and she was seeing it as clearly as Watty. It was an autumn evening and she could smell the burning leaves. She had been told to go back to the house but she had stopped in the trees, and her mother was screaming at her father and he had walked away and Nanny had tried to quieten her mother but she had pushed Nanny back and run into the studio.

Watty was by the bonfire and Nanny had banged on the door and shouted and after a while her mother had rushed out with a picture in her hands and thrown it into the smoke, and something made the flames leap up, and Nanny had gone on shouting and the hiding child had shut her eyes and run for the house. She had watched the bonfire from the nursery window and nobody had come for her for a long time.

The car crash was late at night. She had been bathed and put to bed. Not by Nanny that night, and she had been scolded for not wanting her supper. Her father had probably come back and seen what had happened down there at the studio, and left again, because the crash was near the house. Nanny would know if he had but Mell did not want to know. It was enough to remember that last scene, and her mother's screams when the news came. Next morning Elizabeth was deep in shock, and although nobody realised it so was the child Amelia . . .

'Perhaps I shouldn't have told you this,' said Watty, as she put her hands over her stricken face. He had no idea how much he had told her, by unlocking the memories in her mind. 'But don't let her spoil your life,' he pleaded. 'She'll do anything to keep you here and she'll always put herself first.'

Mell had always known that. Elizabeth was pathologically scared of insecurity, and Mell would always feel a responsibility for her, as towards a wilful and beautiful child.

Poor Watty looked shattered and she put an arm around him and managed to smile. 'Don't worry about me, I'll get out.'

'Not that Gunnison?' Robert would spoil her mother, and Elizabeth and Nanny would spoil him, and Mell said wryly,

'Could be, in a way. But I don't feel like facing them right now. There's something I should be doing at the shop. I think I'll work late tonight.' She left Watty sitting, and at the door she said, 'The paintings were good.'

He fumbled in his pocket for his pipe. 'I don't know about that, I don't know much about pictures. Where did you get them from? We got rid of what was left afterwards because of upsetting her. Not that there was much.'

'I found them in an old bureau in the attic. They're in my workroom now. Nanny said not to let my mother see them.'

He grinned without humour and began to fill his pipe. 'The old crow's right for once.'

The paintings hanging on her wall had an added poignancy tonight. She stood looking at them for a long time, seeing the promise they held. He must have been untrained, all his education had been in preparation for that stockbroking career, but there was talent here. And now other fainter memories came back, of a man with a sensitive face who had carried her around on his shoulders and called her and her mother 'my two pretty birds'. Her mother had loved him, too, she thought, but she had loved security more.

'I'm sorry you didn't get away,' Mell said aloud. And that when he did he had gone in such blinding anger that the car had crashed and he had died. There was irony in that. She would break away without anger but now she was determined to fight for what she wanted; she would take chances and she would not be afraid.

She went back upstairs and rang Anna's number and said, 'I want to take a holiday, any chance of you coming in?' If not, and if Pammie couldn't cope and if she could get no one else, she would shut the shop for a while, but this journey she must make.

Anna said yes, promptly. She had enjoyed the few days while Mell was recovering from excess sunburn. She'd said at the time, any time, and she had meant it, and Mell said she would let her know when she had a firm date, tomorrow probably.

'Where are you going?' Anna enquired and Mell said, 'To the Greek islands.'

She was going to a wedding on Karpathos, because that was the only place she would be sure of finding Barney. Maybe she had intended this all along, but now there was no doubt at all in her mind. She would be there, in her yellow dress, wearing the earrings and the rings he gave her for her birthday. Tomorrow she would call at the travel agents and book a flight and whatever else you needed to get to Karpathos.

The phone rang almost as soon as she replaced it and

Nanny said, 'Are you still there?' although Mell had answered.

'I'm going to be late,' said Mell. 'Stocktaking.' In a way she was taking stock.

'You might have said this morning,' Nanny grumbled. 'I've got your dinner cooked.'

'Sorry about that,' said Mell. 'Give Robert another helping.'

She occupied herself until she could reasonably say she was tired and go straight up to her room if anyone was up when she got home, but the only light burning was in the downstairs hall. Her mother wasn't concerned about her tonight, all the bedroom doors were closed and presumably everyone was sleeping peacefully.

Each night Mell had written her letter. She was on the twelfth page, most of it written neatly but some of the writing scrawled. That was where she had been half asleep, those were the bits she still wasn't sure she wanted him to see because it was dream stuff, erotic and explicit.

Tonight she had something to tell him, what Watty had told her. No one else knew. Watty was no gossip and Nanny would have been shot before she told anything that would put Elizabeth in the wrong. But Mell would have written to Barney about it because she was telling him everything, filling these pages compulsively as though they were a link that musn't be broken.

Tonight she took the pad out of her handbag and sat up in bed, with it balanced on her knees and her pen poised. But she didn't start to write because suddenly Barney seemed to be near her. It was like hearing his step and she looked towards the door, then gave herself an impatient little shake because that was crazy. She knew now when she would be seeing him again and that must be giving her this feeling of closeness.

Or perhaps he was thinking of her. That could happen sometimes when two people were on the same mental wavelength. When she thought of him, which she seemed to do most of the time she wasn't compelled to think of something else, Gemma had to be in the background of her mind because Gemma was with him. So thinking of Barney rarely made Mell happy. But tonight she said, 'Wherever you are, think of me; I'll be with you soon.' Then she put back the pad and the pen and turned out the light . . .

By the time Nanny came down next morning Mell had her breakfast ready. 'Finished your stocktaking?' asked Nanny, lowering herself into a chair, and Mell said,

'Don't cook for me tonight, I shall be out.' She would go round to Anna's. She would not be spending evenings at home for a while because the memories that Watty's concern had brought to life were painful ones. She was not sure she could trust herself not to accuse her mother, blame her for something that had happened all those years ago that was best forgotten. No good could come of that, but when she handed over Elizabeth's early morning tea she heard herself say, 'You shouldn't have destroyed his paintings.'

Her mother was awake. She was sitting up in bed, looking rested and smug, so she heard well enough, but she looked straight into Mell's eyes, over the white and gold teacup, and her voice was puzzled. 'What are you talking about?'

Mell knew she would have to go into every detail before her mother would remember any of it, and even then Elizabeth would say nothing had happened that way. Elizabeth was not to blame, she had done nothing, Mell was mistaken.

Elizabeth had put it all out of her mind long ago. Mell left her with her tea and left early for the shop. Watty had not arrived when she left. When she did see him she would tell him where she planned to be on the seventeenth of next month, and she thought he would approve.

As soon as Pammie arrived Mell said, 'I'm going on

holiday next month. I spoke to Anna last night and she's willing to come in.' Anna was rather too brisk and serious for Pammie's tastes but she said,

'OK, I suppose. Going somewhere nice?'

'To the Greek islands,' said Mell.

'On your own?'

'Uh huh.'

'You might end up with a Greek millionaire,' Pammie chortled and Mell thought, before I leave I will tell you who I am going to end up with, but not just yet; I don't want the news circulating all over town.

The phone was busier than the doorbell this morning. It hardly seemed to stop ringing. There were several business calls, a couple of social calls for Pammie, three for Mell—one girl and two men, all suggesting outings. She committed herself to a party that the girl was giving and said, 'Sorry, but I'm terribly busy,' to Alec Wilton and to somebody else whom she had known for years and who had recently decided she was his type.

Pammie had just gone out to lunch and Mell was finishing serving a customer when the phone rang again. 'It's never stopped this morning,' she told the woman. 'It's been one of those days.'

'Rainbow's End, can I help you?' she said as the woman went out.

'Hallo,' he said and it wasn't the first time she had thought a voice was Barney's, hoping too hard, but this time her heart seemed to jump into her throat and go on beating there.

'It's never you,' she squeaked and he said,

'You won't get many noes to that.'

'Barney?'

'Yes.'

'But you're so clear. It's marvellous. Where are you?'

'I'll tell you where I'll be tonight. At the farm.'

'*The* farm? Whiteheads' farm? The dig?'

'The same.'

'Why?' She was starting to smile so widely that her lips could hardly form the word.

'There's a legal loophole I've got to straighten out.'

'How awful,' she said, grinning like a Cheshire cat.

'Just a couple of signatures, but I've got to be there. Can I see you?'

'What time?' This afternoon she would have been fixing to fly thousands of miles to meet him so she would surely be five miles from here any time he was.

'Can you come straight from the shop?' he asked.

'About six? Yes.'

'Goodbye till then.' She put down the phone very gently as if it might shatter. She went to the door and turned the CLOSED sign and slipped on the latch, then she ran down to the cellars and flung her arms wide and whirled ecstatically round and round from one end of the room to the other. Somebody up there liked her. Somebody was on her side, and God bless all legal loopholes. She wanted to laugh and sing and dance, and say thank you, thank you, thank you, to whatever fates had conspired to bring him back tonight.

She needed most of the lunch hour to calm down, but by the time Pammie returned she was no longer gibbering with excitement, and having got the initial shock out of her system she was almost rational. She could still hardly believe it and it was a kind of superstition that kept her quiet, as if telling Pammie would break the spell. It was magic, and she spent the afternoon hugging her secret and pretending to be busy with the books.

Pammie left early—she had seen a pair of shoes in a shop window and thought she might try them on—and Mell brushed her hair and put more blusher on her cheekbones, and then shut the shop and headed for Ruddington. On the way she caught herself wondering if she had dreamed it, if she would arrive there and they would look at her blankly and say, 'No, we're not expecting him. He's in Greece, isn't he?' Then she would know she was going nuts. But of course she had spoken to Barney; it was just such incredible luck, like winning the pools or opening an oyster on the biggest pearl in the world.

He was waiting for her in the courtyard, in jeans and dark polo-necked sweater, and her first sight of him hit her fiercely and suddenly, leaving her heart and her pulses racing. As he came towards her van she thought, *this is how I know that he is the one person in the world I am meant to be with. Now I am warm and alive again.*

He reached her as she stepped out and she had to hug herself to hold in her joy. She said, 'What a nuisance for you, having to come back. What happened?'

'A small legal hassle.' *God bless all pig-headed men, especially Farmer Whitehead.*

'All right now?'

'Everything's in hand.' He took her hand and she smiled because she felt complete and whole, linked with him as they walked towards the towpath. 'I'm staying in the boathouse,' he said. 'I got used to it while I was here. You're looking well.'

'So are you,' she said brightly. 'You've hardly changed at all. It seems like last week.'

'All well at home?'

'My mother put out a few flags when you left.'

'I can imagine!'

'She says there's something about you that frightens her.'

'There's something about her that frightens me,' he said grimly. 'She's a raving anachronism.'

Out of touch with the times, and he was so right. She laughed. 'I'll look it up later.'

The oaks and the elms and the horse chestnuts were russet, breaking into flame. The river was starting to run high and there was no *Misty* moored under the willows. 'Where's the *Misty*?' she asked.

'Alan and Bridget have taken her up river.'

She had met Alan's Bridget at the party; a nice girl. She said, 'It was a good party. Gemma looked— interesting. Was she wearing a body stocking?' Barney raised an eyebrow. 'Well,' she said, 'I thought you should know, if anybody did. She couldn't find anything she liked in my shop.'

'I don't suppose she could,' he said.

It was very tidy in the boathouse, with nothing scattered around, but warm with a small calor gas stove burning. 'How long will you be here?' she asked and when he said, 'I'm leaving tomorrow,' she was prepared for that and still more than grateful for tonight.

In the kitchen he poured wine into two tumblers and she sat on the sofa holding hers. He put his glass on the table and went to the little round window that overlooked the river and she sensed a tension in him, not pleasurable, as though there would be no joy for her in what he was going to say next. 'I've been talking to Watty,' he said.

Had he gone in through the back gate, avoiding the house? Watty would be flattered. She started to say, 'He asks me every day if I've heard——' when Barney faced her, dark eyes narrowed.

'He says you're seeing a lot of Robert Gunnison. He thinks you might be thinking of marrying him.'

She would never have expected Barney to believe that, she hadn't realised that Watty had. She started to laugh. She was going to explain, but he said, 'You can't do it,' and although this was absurd he was almost frightening, glaring like that. 'It isn't just that the man's too old for you—how old is he by the way, fifty odd?'

She answered the question. 'Younger than that.' Six months older than her mother, actually.

'He could have fooled me,' said Barney. 'I've dug up livelier looking specimens. Shut yourself in with him and you're buried.'

Indeed she would be, but hearing Barney arguing as though this really mattered to him was intoxicating and she couldn't resist saying meekly, 'I'm sure Robert would be a very considerate husband.'

'I shouldn't think he'd be over-demanding.' His voice was scathing, then it took on an acid edge. 'But you'd better decide how you feel about the demands he will make before you get into a situation that could strip you naked with no options and no escape,' and that made her gulp before she could say,

'That does sound pretty grim.'

'More grim than pretty.'

She looked down into the wineglass because she couldn't meet his eyes. She should be saying, 'Robert isn't coming to see me any more,' but she said nothing and he asked, 'They're still trying to pressure you?' She gave a small shrug, still with her eyes downcast, and he said impatiently, 'Then tell them no and clear off for a while if you can't face the music.'

'Clear off where?'

'Come away with me,' and it seemed that that was what she had always been waiting to hear. 'You can stay in my flat.'

'Where Gemma lives?'

'Her parents' home is on the other side of town. You'd like the folk in my house.' She was sure she would. She wondered if he would be there or if he was just offering her a bolt hole for a while, but he went on, 'If you stay with me for a week or two Robert and your mother should get the message,' and she burst out laughing.

'If I stay with you for a weekend everybody will get the message.'

He smiled then, wryly, but it was a grin. 'Right, that's settled. I know it's been a game for you this summer, kicking over the traces, but you can't seriously consider marrying Gunnison.'

She had laughed a lot this summer, she had had fun, she had been happy, but all the time love had been growing and that was the biggest reality of her life. She said, 'Who said it was a game?'

'Your mother for one.' He took a swig of his wine and sat down in one of the armchairs, his expression suddenly a caricature of Elizabeth Beaumont's at her most disapproving while his voice exaggerated her genteel fluting tones. '"I hope you don't think there's any future in this game you're playing with my Amelia because it would be criminal if you persuaded her there was".'

That wasn't what she had told Mell she had said. 'She said that?' Mell croaked.

'Oh, she reminded me of everything you've got going for you here, in case I hadn't noticed.' He was mimicking the voice again. '"This is her home where her roots and traditions are," with all your ancestors looking down. "She needs her family and friends, she's always been a delicate girl".'

'I have *not*,' she yelped.

'No?' He took her word for it, seeing Elizabeth as an overprotective mother whereas she was simply over-possessive. 'But you have led a sheltered life and when you talked about breaking out you weren't expecting too much upheaval were you?' She wanted upheaval, she didn't give a fig for her lifestyle. 'But hearing that you could be marrying Gunnison,' he said, 'that I've got to put a stop to.'

'By talking me out of it?' She leaned towards him and she heard his breath catch. He reached to take her hand and again the current flowed between them and he said quietly,

'Failing that, I could kill him.'

He was joking, she thought. She smiled but he was not smiling as he pulled her against him, and he was kissing her as if they had been parted for years and she wrapped her arms around him, her lips parted hungrily to take the kiss and her body craving to take the man.

It was the best. But then it always was the best. The tenderness and the passion were so overwhelming that she climaxed in pure soaring joy that nothing surely could surpass. Tonight really was like scaling the heights of paradise, and afterwards she lay in her lover's arms, exhausted and fulfilled and dizzy with happiness.

There hadn't been much talking. Words weren't needed when touch was such complete communication, but now he said, 'Will you come with me?'

It was a dark night. The skylight above the bed showed no stars and no moon. Even when she turned her head she could hardly make out his features but she could feel his breath and the hard smooth body encircling her soft bare skin. 'Oh yes,' she said.

'To the islands, not just the flat?' It would be like that dream on her birthday night, of the sea-going boat that would take them anywhere in the world.

Even if Gemma was aboard she was going. 'Where's Gemma?' she asked and he said,

'I have no idea. She's finally given me up as a dead loss.' She gurgled with amusement against his shoulder, tasting the salt of his skin, teasing.

'I wouldn't say that. How could anyone say that?'

He sat up, looking at her, and maybe he could see in the dark better than she could because he said, 'You're beautiful, you know that? You lit up the world that night.'

She said wistfully, 'It was the first time for me, but not for you,' and he said,

'I'd never had you before, I'd been waiting for you.' Then he lay down again beside her, hands under his head on the pillow, staring up at the skylight, and she propped herself on an elbow to listen to what he had to tell her.

'I spent the first fourteen years of my life waiting for my folk to turn up. They never did, and then when I got used to being lonely I got lucky. Good teachers.' He grinned; she saw the flash of white teeth. 'Good memory; I passed the exams and got the breaks, and after a while I could go anywhere I wanted, do anything. But I remembered the waiting and I wasn't going to risk that kind of loneliness again.

'Now I've no choice because I want you more than anything in the world and I'll never stop wanting you. You do have a sheltered life here and maybe that's what you want; your mother certainly thinks it is, and you kept well away from me the night I was leaving.'

Her lips parted to speak as he went on. 'I asked Watty to let me know if you were all right, if everything was all right with you, and he phoned me yesterday and told me that Gunnison was still around and you might——' He stopped there, then said, '*marry him*', as though he was realising now how preposterous that was.

'Don't be daft,' she said, and they laughed, until the tears were running down her cheeks and they were both gasping for breath. 'How did Watty get in touch?' she asked, between hiccups.

'He rang the flat,' said Barney. 'I've been working there. I didn't fly out last Sunday, and if Watty hadn't rung me I'd still be here about now because there's no point me going without you, there's nothing out there without you.'

He had come back for her, it was nothing to do with the dig, and she asked, 'Wasn't there a legal loophole?'

'There was,' he said, 'needing both our signatures. You hadn't married me.'

'Are you serious?'

'I am.' He drew her down again, cradling her gently against him. 'All right, you're not, but give me time. I'll ask you at breakfast on the *Cormorant* every morning until you get used to the idea.' He spoke the words into her hair. '"Sweetheart," I'll say, "will you be my wife?"'

When they reached Karpathos she would say to him, 'I would have been here, waiting for you,' but she had to tell him before how completely and faithfully she loved him. She said, 'I've got a letter I wrote for you. You can turn on the light if you like, but I can remember what I said and if you hold me close I'll tell you.'

Anne Mather's
latest
masterpiece

From the author of a string of best sellers including 'Hidden in the Flame' with sales currently exceeding 90 million copies, comes The Longest Pleasure. The torrid story of two proud individuals bound by the extreme forces of love … and hate.

W⭕RLDWIDE

The Longest Pleasure is longer than the usual passionate tale, at a price of only £3.50.   Available from August 1986

Her secret from the past unlocked the door to her future.

In the Venice of 1819, the Contessa Allegra di Rienz gave her love to the scandalous poet Lord Byron and left the legacy of a daughter he would never know.

Over 100 years later Allegra Brent discovered the secret of her ancestors and travelled to Venice in search o di Rienzi's heirs. There she met the bloodstirring Conte Renaldo di Rienzi and relived the passionate romance tha started so long before.

WORLDWIDE

LEGACY OF PASSION.
Another longer romance for your enjoyment.
AVAILABLE FROM SEPTEMBER 1986. PRICE £2.95